CATALYST the pearson custom library for chemistry

Owens Community College
CHM 105
Chemistry for Biological Life Sciences

PEARSON

Cover Art: Courtesy of Photodisc, Age Fotostock America, Inc., and Photo Researchers, and Getty Images.

Copyright © 2013 by Pearson Learning Solutions
All rights reserved.

Permission in writing must be obtained from the publisher before any part of this work may be reproduced or transmitted in any form or by any means, electronic or mechanical, including photocopying and recording, or by any information storage or retrieval system.

Additional copyright information is included, where applicable, as a footnote at the beginning of each chapter.

Pyrex, pHydrion, Chem3D Plus, Apple, Macintosh, Chemdraw, Hypercard, graphTool, Corning, Teflon, Mel-Temp, Rotaflow, Tygon, Spec20, and LambdaII UV/Vis are registered trademarks.

Chem3D Plus is a registered trademark of the Cambridge Soft Corp.

The information, illustrations, and/or software contained in this book, and regarding the above mentioned programs, are provided "as is," without warranty of any kind, express or implied, including without limitation any warranty concerning the accuracy, adequacy, or completeness of such information. Neither the publisher, the authors, nor the copyright holders shall be responsible for any claims attributable to errors, omissions, or other inaccuracies contained in this book. Nor shall they be liable for direct, indirect, special, incidental, or consequential damages arising out of the use of such information or material.

The authors and publisher believe that the lab experiments described in this publication, when conducted in conformity with the safety precautions described herein and according to the school's laboratory safety procedures, are reasonably safe for the students for whom this manual is directed. Nonetheless, many of the described experiments are accompanied by some degree of risk, including human error, the failure or misuse of laboratory or electrical equipment, mismeasurement, spills of chemicals, and exposure to sharp objects, heat, body fluids, blood or other biologics. The authors and publisher disclaim any liability arising from such risks in connections with any of the experiments contained in this manual. If students have questions or problems with materials, procedures, or instructions on any experiment, they should always ask their instructor for help before proceeding.

This special edition published in cooperation with Pearson Learning Solutions.

Printed in the United States of America.

Please visit our website at *www.pearsonlearningsolutions.com*.

Attention bookstores: For permission to return unused stock, contact us at *pe-uscustomreturns@pearson.com*.

Pearson Learning Solutions, 501 Boylston Street, Suite 900, Boston, MA 02116
A Pearson Education Company
www.pearsoned.com

ISBN 10: 1-256-61139-5
ISBN 13: 978-1-256-61139-4

Table of Contents

Working Safely in the Laboratory

The chemistry laboratory, with its equipment, glassware, and chemicals, has the potential for accidents. In order to avoid accidents, precautions must be taken by every student to ensure the safety of everyone working in the laboratory. By following the rules for handling chemicals safely and carrying out only the approved procedures, you will create a safe environment in the laboratory. After you have read the following sections, complete the safety quiz and the questions on laboratory equipment. Then sign and submit the commitment to lab safety.

A. Preparing for Laboratory Work

Pre-read Before you come to the laboratory, read the discussion of and directions for the experiment you will be doing. Make sure you know what the experiment is about before you start the actual work. If you have a question, ask your instructor to clarify the procedures.

Do assigned work only Do only the experiments that have been assigned by your instructor. No unauthorized experiments are to be carried out in the laboratory. Experiments are done at assigned times, unless you have an open lab situation. Your instructor must approve any change in procedure.

Do not work alone in a laboratory.

Safety awareness Learn the location and use of the emergency eyewash fountains, the emergency shower, fire blanket, fire extinguishers, and exits. Memorize their locations in the laboratory. Be aware of other students in the lab carrying chemicals to their desk or to a balance.

 APPROVED EYE PROTECTION IS REQUIRED AT ALL TIMES!

Safety goggles must be worn all the time you are in the lab The particular type depends on state law, which usually requires industrial-quality eye protection. Contact lenses may be worn in the lab if needed for therapeutic reasons, provided that **safety goggles** are worn over the contact lenses. Contact lenses without goggles are dangerous because splashed chemicals make them difficult to remove. If chemicals accumulate under a lens, permanent eye damage can result. If a chemical should splash into your eyes, flood the eyes with water at the eyewash fountain. Continue to rinse with water for at least 10 minutes.

Wear protective clothing Wear sensible clothing in the laboratory. Loose sleeves, shorts, or open-toed shoes can be dangerous. A lab coat is useful in protecting clothes and covering arms. Wear shoes that cover your feet to prevent glass cuts; wear long pants and long-sleeved shirts to protect skin. Long hair should be tied back so it does not fall into chemicals or a flame from a Bunsen burner.

No food or drink is allowed at any time in the laboratory Do not let your friends or children visit while you are working in the lab; have them wait outside.

Prepare your work area Before you begin a lab, clear the lab bench or work area of all your personal items, such as backpacks, books, sweaters, and coats. Find a storage place in the lab for them. All you will need is your laboratory manual, calculator, pen or pencil, text, and equipment from your lab drawer.

B. Handling Chemicals Safely

Check labels twice Be sure you take the correct chemical. *DOUBLE-CHECK THE LABEL* on the bottle before you remove a chemical from its container. For example, sodium sulfate (Na_2SO_4) could be mistaken for sodium sulfite (Na_2SO_3) if the label is not read carefully.

Use small amounts of chemicals Pour or transfer a chemical into a small, clean container (beaker, test tube, flask, etc.) available in your lab drawer. To avoid contamination of the chemical reagents, never insert droppers, pipets, or spatulas into the reagent bottles. Take only the quantity of chemical you need for the experiment. Do not keep a reagent bottle at your desk; *return* it to its proper location in the laboratory. Label the container. Many containers have etched sections on which you can write in pencil. If not, use tape or a marking pencil.

Do not return chemicals to the original containers To avoid contamination of chemicals, dispose of used chemicals according to your instructor's instructions. *Never return unused chemicals to reagent bottles.* Some liquids and water-soluble compounds may be washed down the sink with plenty of water, but check with your instructor first. Dispose of organic compounds in specially marked containers in the hoods.

Do not taste chemicals; smell a chemical cautiously Never use any equipment in the drawer such as a beaker to drink from. When required to note the odor of a chemical, first take a deep breath of fresh air and hold it while you use your hand to fan some vapors toward your nose and note the odor. Do not inhale the fumes directly. If a compound gives off an irritating vapor, use it in the fume hood to avoid exposure.

Do not shake laboratory thermometers Laboratory thermometers respond quickly to the temperature of their environment. Shaking a thermometer is unnecessary and can cause breakage.

Liquid spills Spills of water or liquids at your work area or floor should be cleaned up immediately. Small spills of liquid chemicals can be cleaned up with a paper towel. Large chemical spills must be treated with absorbing material such as cat litter. Place the contaminated material in a waste disposal bag and label it. If a liquid chemical is spilled on the skin, flood *immediately with water* for at least 10 minutes. Any clothing soaked with a chemical must be removed immediately because an absorbed chemical can continue to damage the skin.

Mercury spills The cleanup of mercury requires special attention. Mercury spills may occur from broken thermometers. Notify your instructor immediately of any mercury spills so that special methods can be used to clean up the mercury. Place any free mercury and mercury cleanup material in special containers for mercury only.

Laboratory accidents Always notify your instructor of any chemical spill or accident in the laboratory. Broken glass can be swept up with a brush and pan and placed in a specially labeled container for broken glass. Cuts are the most common injuries in a lab. If a cut should occur, wash, elevate, and apply pressure if necessary. Always inform your instructor of any laboratory accident.

Clean up Wash glassware as you work. Begin your cleanup 15 minutes before the end of the laboratory session. Return any borrowed equipment to the stockroom. Be sure that you always turn off the gas and water at your work area. Make sure you leave a clean desk. Check the balance you used. *Wash your hands before you leave the laboratory.*

C. Heating Chemicals Safely

Heat only heat-resistant glassware Only glassware marked Pyrex® or Kimax® can be heated; other glassware may shatter. To heat a substance in a test tube, use a test tube holder. Holding the test tube at an angle, move it continuously through the flame. Never point the open end of the test tube at anyone or look directly into it. A hot piece of iron or glass looks the same as it does at room temperature. Place a hot object on a tile or a wire screen to cool.

Flammable liquids Never heat a flammable liquid over an open flame. If heating is necessary, your instructor will indicate the use of a steam bath or a hot plate.

Never heat a closed container When a closed system is heated, it can explode as pressure inside builds.

Fire Small fires can be extinguished by covering them with a watch glass. If a larger fire is involved, use a fire extinguisher to douse the flames. *Do not direct a fire extinguisher at other people in the laboratory.* Shut off gas burners in the laboratory. When working in a lab, tie long hair back away from the face. If someone else's clothing or hair catches on fire, get them to the floor and roll them into a fire blanket. They may also be placed under the safety shower to extinguish flames. Cold water or ice may be applied to small burns.

D. Waste Disposal

As you work in the laboratory, chemical wastes are produced. Although we will use small quantities of materials, some waste products are unavoidable. To dispose of these chemical wastes safely, you need to know some general rules for chemical waste disposal.

Metals Metals should be placed in a container to be recycled.

Nonhazardous chemical wastes Substances such as sodium chloride (NaCl) that are soluble in water and are not hazardous may be emptied into the sink. If the waste is a solid, dissolve it in water before disposal.

Hazardous chemical wastes If a substance is hazardous or not soluble in water, it must be placed in a container that is labeled for waste disposal. Your instructor will inform you if chemical wastes are hazardous and identify the proper waste containers. *If you are not sure about the proper disposal of a substance, ask your instructor.* The labels on a waste container should indicate if the contents are hazardous, the name of the chemical waste, and the date that the container was placed in the lab.

Hazard rating The general hazards of a chemical are presented in a spatial arrangement of numbers with the flammability rating at twelve o'clock, the reactivity rating at the three o'clock position, and the health rating at the nine o'clock position. At the six o'clock position, information may be given on the reactivity of the substance with water. If there is unusual reactivity with water, the symbol W̶ (do not mix with water) is shown. In the laboratory, you may see these ratings in color with blue for health hazard, red for flammability, and yellow for reactivity hazards.

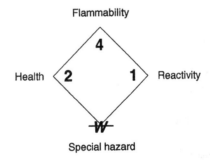

A chemical is assigned a relative hazard rating that ranges from 1 (little hazard) to 4 (extreme hazard). The health hazard indicates the likelihood that a material will cause injury due to exposure by contact, inhalation, or ingestion. The flammability hazard indicates the potential for burning. The reactivity hazard indicates the instability of the material by itself or with water with subsequent release of energy. Special hazards may be included such as W̶ for reactivity with water or OX for oxidizing properties.

E. Safety Quiz

The safety quiz will review the preceding safety discussion. Circle the correct answer(s) in each of the following questions. Check your answers on page xiii.

1. Approved eye protection is to be worn
   a. For certain experiments
   b. Only for hazardous experiments
   c. All the time

2. Eating in the laboratory is
   a. Not permitted
   b. Allowed at lunch time
   c. All right if you are careful

3. If you need to smell a chemical, you should
   a. Inhale deeply over the test tube
   b. Take a breath of air and fan the vapors toward you
   c. Put some of the chemical in your hand, and smell it

4. When heating liquids in a test tube, you should
   a. Move the tube back and forth through the flame
   b. Look directly into the open end of the test tube to see what is happening
   c. Direct the open end of the tube away from other students

5. Unauthorized experiments are
   a. All right as long as they don't seem hazardous
   b. All right as long as no one finds out
   c. Not allowed

6. If a chemical is spilled on your skin, you should
   a. Wait to see if it stings
   b. Flood the area with water for 10 minutes
   c. Add another chemical to absorb it

7. When taking liquids from a reagent bottle,
   a. Insert a dropper
   b. Pour the reagent into a small container
   c. Put back what you don't use

8. In the laboratory, open-toed shoes and shorts are
   a. Okay if the weather is hot
   b. All right if you wear a lab apron
   c. Dangerous and should not be worn

9. When is it all right to taste a chemical?
   a. Never
   b. When the chemical is not hazardous
   c. When you use a clean beaker

10. After you use a reagent bottle,
    a. Keep it at your desk in case you need more
    b. Return it to its proper location
    c. Play a joke on your friends and hide it

4

11. Before starting an experiment,
    a. Read the entire procedure
    b. Ask your lab partner how to do the experiment
    c. Skip to the laboratory report and try to figure out what to do

12. Working alone in the laboratory without supervision is
    a. All right if the experiment is not too hazardous
    b. Not allowed
    c. Allowed if you are sure you can complete the experiment without help

13. You should wash your hands
    a. Only if they are dirty
    b. Before eating lunch in the lab
    c. Before you leave the lab

14. Personal items (books, sweater, etc.) should be
    a. Kept on your lab bench
    b. Left outside
    c. Stored out of the way, not on the lab bench

15. When you have taken too much of a chemical, you should
    a. Return the excess to the reagent bottle
    b. Store it in your lab locker for future use
    c. Discard it using proper disposal procedures

16. In the lab, you should wear
    a. Practical, protective clothing
    b. Something fashionable
    c. Shorts and loose-sleeved shirts

17. If a chemical is spilled on the table,
    a. Clean it up right away
    b. Let the stockroom help clean it up
    c. Use appropriate adsorbent if necessary

18. If mercury is spilled,
    a. Pick it up with a dropper
    b. Call your instructor
    c. Push it under the table where no one can see it

19. If your hair or shirt catches on fire, you should
    a. Use the safety shower to extinguish the flames
    b. Drop to the ground and roll
    c. Use the fire blanket to put it out

20. A hazardous waste should be
    a. Placed in a special waste container
    b. Washed down the drain
    c. Placed in the wastebasket

Answer Key to Safety Quiz

1. c	2. a	3. b	4. a, c	5. c	6. b	7. b
8. c	9. a	10. b	11. a	12. b	13. c	14. c
15. c	16. a	17. a, c	18. b	19. a, b, c	20. c	

Commitment to Safety in the Laboratory

✔ **I have read the laboratory preparation and safety procedures and agree that I will comply with the safety rules by carrying out the following:**

_____ Read laboratory instructions ahead of lab time.

_____ Know the locations of eyewash fountains, fire extinguishers, safety showers, and exits.

_____ Wear safety goggles or safety glasses in the laboratory at all times.

_____ Use the proper equipment for laboratory procedures.

_____ Never perform any unauthorized experiments or work alone in the laboratory.

_____ Remember what is hot if I have used the Bunsen burner or hot plate.

_____ Clean up chemical spills and broken glass immediately.

_____ Immediately inform the instructor of a chemical spill or accident in the laboratory.

_____ Never eat or drink in the laboratory.

_____ Wear sensible clothing and closed shoes, and tie back long hair in the laboratory.

_____ Read the labels on reagent bottles carefully, remove only small amounts of reagent with the proper tools, and never return unused chemical to the bottle.

_____ Dispose of broken glass and waste chemicals in the appropriate waste container.

_____ Wash my hands and leave a clean work area when I leave the lab.

_____ Never leave an experiment when substances are heating or reacting.

_____
your signature

_____   _____
laboratory class and section   date

F. Laboratory Equipment

When experiments call for certain pieces of equipment, it is important that you know which item to select. Using the wrong piece of equipment can lead to errors in measurement or cause a procedure to be done incorrectly. For safety and proper results, you need to identify the laboratory items you will use in doing lab work.

Look for each of the items shown in the pictures of laboratory equipment on pages xvi–xvii. The quiz will help you learn some of the common laboratory equipment.

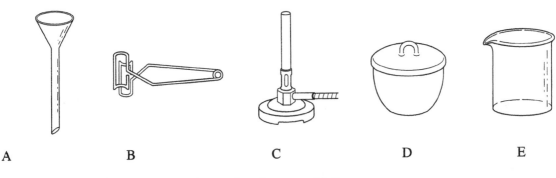

A   B   C   D   E

1.   Match each of the above pieces of equipment with its name:

_____ Bunsen burner   _____ test tube holder   _____ beaker

_____ crucible   _____ funnel

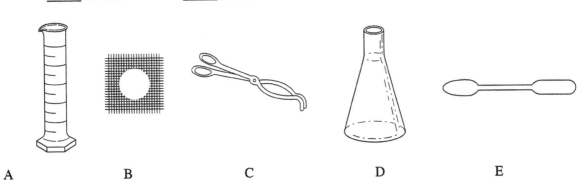

A   B   C   D   E

2.   Match each of the above pieces of equipment with its use in the laboratory:

_____ Used to hold liquids and to carry out reactions

_____ Used to pick up a crucible

_____ Used to support a beaker on an iron ring during heating

_____ Used to transfer small amounts of a solid substance

_____ Used to measure the volume of a liquid

A Visual Guide to Laboratory Equipment

Evaporating dish
Used to evaporate a solution
to dryness

Crucible and cover
Used to heat small samples
to high temperatures

Crucible tongs
Used to pick up a crucible

Watch glass
Used to cover a beaker or
to hold a small amount of
a substance

Stirring rod
Used to mix or combine two or more
substances in a test tube or a beaker

Forceps
Used to pick up a small object
or one that is hot

Pinch clamp
Used to close rubber tubing

Spatula
Used to transfer small amounts
of a solid

File
Used to cut glass tubing

Thermometer
Used to measure the
temperature of a
substance

Pipet
Used to transfer a specific
volume of liquid solution
to a container

Buret
Used to deliver a measured
amount of solution with a
known concentration

Medicine dropper
Used to deliver drops
of a solution or liquid

A Visual Guide to Laboratory Equipment

Beaker   **Erlenmeyer flask**   **Florence flask**
Used to hold solids or liquids and to carry out reactions

Graduated cylinder
Used to measure out accurate volumes of liquid

Wide-mouth bottle
Used to contain a gas or for reactions

Funnel
Used to transfer liquids to another container and when filtering out solids

Shell vial
Used to hold small amounts of solid substances

Bunsen burner
Used to provide heat

Ring support stand with clay triangle
Used to support triangle or wire gauze during the heating process

Test tube
A small container for solutions and reactions

Test tube brush
Used to clean a test tube

Wire gauze
Used to support a beaker on an iron ring during heating

Test tube holder
Used to hold a test tube during heating or while still hot

Striker
Used to ignite the gas in a Bunsen burner

Test tube rack
Used to hold and store test tubes

Clamp
Used to hold a buret, test tube, or flask to a ring stand

Heat-resistant tile
Used to set hot objects on during cooling

Measurement and Significant Figures

Goals

- Identify metric units used in measurement such as gram, meter, centimeter, millimeter, and milliliter.
- Correctly read a meterstick, a balance, and a graduated cylinder.
- State the correct number of significant figures in a measurement.

Discussion

Scientists and allied health personnel carry out laboratory procedures, take measurements, and report results accurately and clearly. How well they do these things can mean life or death to a patient. The system of measurement used in science, hospitals, and clinics is the metric system. The metric system is a *decimal system* in which measurements of each type are related by factors of 10. You use a decimal system when you change U.S. money. For example, 1 dime is the same as 10 cents or one cent is 1/10 of a dime. A dime and a cent are related by a factor of 10.

The metric system has one standard unit for each type of measurement. For example, the metric unit of length is the meter, whereas the U.S. system of measurement uses many units of length such as inch, foot, yard, and mile. Most of the rest of the world uses the metric system only. The most common metric units are listed in Table 1.

Table 1 *Metric Units*

Measurement	Metric Unit	Symbol
Length	meter	m
Mass	gram	g
Volume	liter	L
Temperature	degrees Celsius; kelvins	°C; K
Time	second	s

A unit must always be included when reporting a measurement. For example, 5.0 m indicates a quantity of 5.0 meters. Without the unit, we would not know the system of measurement used to obtain the number 5.0. It could have been 5.0 feet, 5.0 kilometers, or 5.0 inches. Thus, a unit is required to complete the measurement reported.

For larger and smaller measurements, prefixes are attached in front of the standard unit. Some prefixes such as *kilo* are used for larger quantities; other prefixes such as *milli* are used for smaller quantities. The most common prefixes are listed in Table 2.

Table 2 *Some Prefixes in the Metric System*

Prefix	Symbol	Meaning
kilo	k	1000
deci	d	0.1 (1/10)
centi	c	0.01 (1/100)
milli	m	0.001 (1/1000)

From *Essential Laboratory Manual for Chemistry: An Introduction to General, Organic, and Biological Chemistry*, Ninth Edition, Karen C. Timberlake. Copyright © 2007 by Pearson Education, Inc. Published by Benjamin Cummings. All rights reserved.

Measured and Exact Numbers

When we measure the length, volume, or mass of an object, the numbers we report are called *measured numbers*. Suppose you got on a scale this morning and saw that you weighed 145 lb. The scale is a measuring tool and your weight is a measured number. Each time we use a measuring tool to determine a quantity, the result is a measured number.

Exact numbers are obtained when we count objects. Suppose you counted 5 beakers in your laboratory drawer. The number 5 is an exact number. You did not use a measuring tool to obtain the number. Exact numbers are also found in the numbers that define a relationship between two metric units or between two U.S. units. For example, the numbers in the following definitions are exact: 1 meter is equal to 100 cm; 1 foot has 12 inches. See Sample Problem 1.

Sample Problem 1

Describe each of the following as a measured or exact number:
a. 14 inches   b. 14 pencils   c. 60 minutes in 1 hour   d. 7.5 kg

Solution:
a. measured   b. exact   c. exact (definition)   d. measured

Significant Figures in Measurements

In measured numbers, all the reported figures are called *significant figures*. The first significant figure is the first nonzero digit. The last significant figure is always the estimated digit. Zeros between other digits or at the end of a decimal number are counted as significant figures. However, leading zeros are *not significant;* they are placeholders. Zeros are *not significant* in large numbers with no decimal points; they are placeholders needed to express the magnitude of the number.

When a number is written in scientific notation, all the figures in the coefficient are significant. Examples of counting significant figures in measured numbers are in Table 3 and Sample Problem 2.

Table 3   *Examples of Counting Significant Figures*

Measurement	Number of Significant Figures	Reason
455.2 cm	4	All nonzero digits are significant.
0.80 m	2	A following zero in a decimal number is significant.
50.2 L	3	A zero between nonzero digits is significant.
0.0005 lb	1	Leading zeros are not significant.
25,000 ft	2	Placeholder zeros are not significant.

Sample Problem 2

State the number of significant figures in each of the following measured numbers:
a. 0.00580 m   b. 132.08 g

Solution:
a. Three significant figures. The zeros after the decimal point are placeholder zeros, but the zero following nonzero digits is *significant.*
b. Five significant figures. The zero between nonzero digits is significant.

When you use a meterstick or read the volume in a graduated cylinder, the measurement must be reported as precisely as possible. The number of *significant figures* you can report depends on the lines marked on the measuring tool you use. For example, on a 50-mL graduated cylinder, the small lines represent a 1-mL volume. If the liquid level is between 21 mL and 22 mL, you know you can report 21 mL for certain. However, you can add one more digit (*the last digit*) to your reported value by estimating between the 1-mL lines. For example, if the volume level were halfway between the 21-mL and 22-mL lines, you would report the volume as 21.5 mL. If the volume level *is exactly* on the 21-mL line, you indicate this precision by adding a *significant zero* to give a measured volume of 21.0 mL.

A. Measuring Length

The standard unit of length in the metric system is the *meter* (*m*). Using an appropriate prefix, you can indicate a length that is greater or less than a meter as listed in Table 4. Kilometers are used in most countries for measuring the distance between two cities, whereas centimeters or millimeters are used for small lengths.

Table 4 *Some Metric Units Used to Measure Length*

Length	Symbol	Meaning
1 kilometer	km	1000 meters (m)
1 decimeter	dm	0.1 m (1/10 m)
1 centimeter	cm	0.01 m (1/100 m)
1 millimeter	mm	0.001 m (1/1000 m)

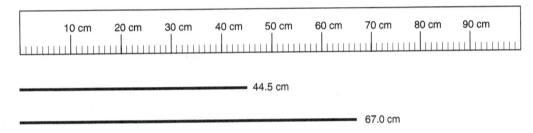

Figure 1 A meterstick divided into centimeters (cm)

A *meterstick* is divided into 100 cm as seen in Figure 1. The smallest lines are centimeters. That means that each measurement you make can be certain to the centimeter. The final digit in a precise measurement is obtained by estimating. For example, the shorter line in Figure 1 reaches the 44-cm mark and is about halfway to 45 cm. We report its length as 44.5 cm. The last digit (0.5) is the estimated digit. If the line appears to end at a centimeter mark, then the estimated digit is 0.0 cm. The longer line in Figure 1 appears to end right at the 67-cm line, which is indicated by reporting its length as 67.0 cm.

B. Measuring Volume

The volume of a substance measures the space it occupies. In the metric system, the unit for volume is the *liter* (*L*). Prefixes are used to express smaller volumes such as deciliters (dL) or milliliters (mL). One cubic centimeter (cm^3 or cc) is equal to 1 mL. The terms are used interchangeably. See Table 5.

Table 5 *Some Metric Units Used to Measure Volume*

Unit of Volume	Symbol	Meaning
1 kiloliter	kL	1000 liters (L)
1 deciliter	dL	0.1 L (1/10 L)
1 milliliter	mL	0.001 L (1/1000 L)

In the laboratory, the volume of a liquid is measured in a graduated cylinder (Figure 2). Set the cylinder on a level surface and bring your eyes even with the liquid level. Notice that the water level is not a straight line but curves downward in the center. This curve, called a *meniscus*, is read at its lowest point (center) to obtain the correct volume measurement for the liquid. In this graduated cylinder, the volume of the liquid is 42.0 mL.

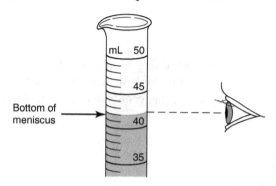

Figure 2   Reading a volume of 42.0 mL in a graduated cylinder

On large cylinders, the lines may represent volumes of 2 mL, 5 mL, or 10 mL. On a 250-mL cylinder, the marked lines usually represent 5 mL. On a 1000-mL cylinder, each line may be 10 mL. Then your precision on a measurement will be to the milliliter or mL.

C.   Measuring Mass

The *mass* of an object indicates the amount of matter present in that object. The *weight* of an object is a measure of the attraction that Earth has for that object. Because this attraction is proportional to the mass of the object, we will use the terms *mass* and *weight* interchangeably.

In the metric system, the unit of mass is the *gram (g)*. A larger unit, the *kilogram (kg)*, is used in measuring a patient's weight in a hospital. A smaller unit of mass, the *milligram (mg)*, is often used in the laboratory. See Table 6.

Table 6   *Some Metric Units Used to Measure Mass*

Mass	Symbol	Meaning
kilogram	kg	1000 g
gram	g	1000 mg
milligram	mg	1/1000 g (0.001 g)

Lab Information

Time: 2 hr

Comments: Tear out the report sheets and place them beside the experimental procedures
as you work.
Determine the markings on each measuring tool before you measure.
Record all the possible numbers for a measurement including an estimated digit.
Write a unit of measurement after each measured number.

Related Topics: Significant figures, measured and exact numbers, metric prefixes

Experimental Procedures

A. Measuring Length

Materials: Meterstick, string

A.1 Observe the marked lines on a meterstick. Identify the lines that represent centimeters and millimeters. Determine how you will estimate between the smallest lines.

A.2 Use the meterstick to make the length measurements (cm) indicated on the report sheet. String may be used to determine the distance around your wrist. Include the estimated digit in each measurement.

A.3 Indicate the estimated digit and the number of significant figures in each measurement. See Sample Problem 3.

Sample Problem 3

What is the estimated digit in each of the following measured lengths?

a. height 1.88 m   b. pencil 11.6 cm

Solution:

a. hundredths place (0.08 g)   b. tenths place (0.6 g)

A.4 Measure the length of the line on the report sheet. List the measurements of the same line obtained by other students in the lab.

B. Measuring Volume

Materials: Display of graduated cylinders with liquids, 50-mL, 100-mL, 250-mL, and 500-mL (or larger) graduated cylinders, test tube, solid object

B.1 **Volume of a liquid** Determine the volumes of the liquids in a display of graduated cylinders. Be as precise as you can. For example, each line marked on a 50-mL graduated cylinder measures 1 mL. By estimating the volume *between* the 1-mL markings, you can report a volume to a tenth (0.1) of a milliliter. Indicate the estimated digit and the number of significant figures in each measurement.

B.2 **Volume of a test tube** Fill a small test tube to the rim. Carefully pour the water into a small graduated cylinder. State the volume represented by the smallest marked lines on the cylinder. Record the volume of the water and state the estimated digit. Fill the test tube again and pour the water into a medium-sized graduated cylinder. Record. Repeat this process using a large graduated cylinder. Record.

B.3 **Volume of a solid by volume displacement** When an object is submerged in water, it displaces its own volume of water, causing the water level to rise. The volume of the object is the difference in the water level before and after the object is submerged. See Figure 3.

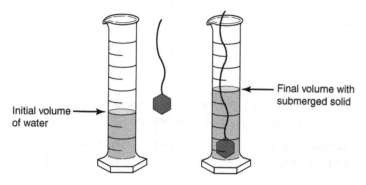

Initial volume
of water

Final volume with
submerged solid

Figure 3 Using volume displacement to determine the volume of a solid

Obtain a graduated cylinder that will hold the solid. Place water in the graduated cylinder until it is about half full. Carefully record the volume of water. Tie a piece of thread around a heavy solid object. Slowly submerge the solid under the water. Record the new volume of the water. Calculate the volume (mL) displaced by the solid.

C. Measuring Mass

Materials: Balance, objects to weigh (beaker, rubber stopper, evaporating dish), unknown mass

C.1 After your instructor shows you how to use a laboratory balance, determine the mass of the listed objects from your lab drawer. If you are using a triple beam balance, be sure that all of your recorded measurements include an estimated digit.

C.2 Now that you have used the balance several times, obtain an object of unknown mass from your instructor. Record the code number and determine its mass. Record. Check your result with the instructor.

Report Sheet

Date _____   Name _____

Section _____   Team _____

Instructor _____   _____

Pre-Lab Study Questions

1. What are the standard units of length, mass, volume, and temperature in the metric (SI) system?

2. Why is the metric system called a decimal system of measurement?

3. What is the purpose of using prefixes in the metric system?

4. Give the name or the abbreviation for each metric unit listed. State the property that it measures.

Name of Unit	Abbreviation	Property Measured
_____	L	_____
centimeter	_____	_____
_____	km	_____
_____	mg	_____

5. Describe each of the following as a measured number or an exact number:

5 books _____   12 roses   _____

5 lb _____   12 inches in 1 foot _____

9.25 g _____   361 miles   _____

0.035 kg _____   100 cm in 1 m   _____

6. How do you determine the last digit in any measured number?

Report Sheet

A. Measuring Length

A.1 What units are represented by the numbers marked on the meterstick? _____

What do the small lines marked on the meterstick represent? _____

Complete the following statements:

There are _____ centimeters (cm) in 1 meter (m).

There are _____ millimeters (mm) in 1 meter (m).

There are _____ millimeters (mm) in 1 centimeter (cm).

A.2

Item	Length	A.3 Estimated Digit	Number of Significant Figures
Width of little fingernail	_____	_____	_____
Distance around your wrist	_____	_____	_____
Length of your shoe	_____	_____	_____
Your height	_____	_____	_____

A.4 Length of line

Your measurement _____

Other students' values _____ _____

_____ _____

Questions and Problems

Q.1 What digits in the measurements for the line by other students are the same as yours and which are different?

Q.2 Why could the measured values obtained by other students be different from yours?

Report Sheet

B. Measuring Volume

B.1 **Volume of a liquid** (*Include units for every measurement*)

	Cylinder 1	Cylinder 2	Cylinder 3
Volume (mL)			

B.2 **Volume of a test tube**

	Small Cylinder _____ mL	Medium Cylinder _____ mL	Large Cylinder _____ mL
Volume represented by smallest line			
Volume (mL) of water in test tube			
Estimated digit			

Which cylinder is the best choice for measuring the volume of water in a test tube? Explain.

B.3 **Volume of a solid by volume displacement**

Volume of water _____

Volume of water and submerged solid _____

Volume of solid _____

C. Measuring Mass

Item	Mass	Number of Significant Figures

C.1 Beaker _____   _____

Stopper _____   _____

Evaporating dish _____   _____

C.2 Unknown #____ _____   _____

Questions and Problems

Q.3 State the number of significant figures in each of the following measurements:

4.5 m _____   204.52 g _____

0.0004 L _____   625 000 mm _____

805 lb _____   34.80 km _____

Q.4 Indicate the estimated digit in each of the following measurements:

1.5 cm _____   4500 mi _____

0.0782 m _____   42.50 g _____

Conversion Factors in Calculations

Goals

- Round off a calculated answer to the correct number of significant figures.
- Determine the area of a rectangle and the volume of a solid by direct measurement.
- Determine metric and metric-to-U.S.-unit equalities and corresponding conversion factors.
- Use conversion factors in calculations to convert units of length, volume, and mass.
- Measure temperature using the Celsius temperature scale.
- Convert a Celsius temperature reading to its Fahrenheit and Kelvin temperatures.

Discussion

As you begin to perform laboratory experiments, you will make measurements, collect data, and carry out calculations. When you use measured numbers in calculations, the answers that you report must reflect the precision of the original measurements. Thus it is often necessary to adjust the results you see on the calculator display. Every time you use your calculator, you will need to assess the mathematical operations, count significant figures, and round off calculator results.

A. Rounding Off

Usually there are fewer significant figures in the measured numbers used in a calculation than there are digits that appear in a calculator display. Therefore, we adjust the calculator result by rounding off. If the first number to be dropped is *less than 5,* it and all following numbers are dropped. If the first number to be dropped is *5 or greater,* the numbers are dropped and the value of the last *retained* digit is increased by 1. When you round a large number, the correct magnitude is retained by replacing the dropped digits with *placeholder zeros.* See Sample Problem 1. When a whole number appears in the calculator display, significant zeros may be added.

Sample Problem 1

Round off each of the following calculator displays to report an answer with three significant figures and another answer with two significant figures:

a. 75.6243   b. 0.528392   c. 387,600   d. 4

Solution:	Three Significant Figures	Two Significant Figures
a.	75.6	76
b.	0.528	0.53
c.	388 000	390 000
d.	4.00	4.0

B. Significant Figures in Calculations

When you carry out mathematical operations, the answer you report depends on the number of significant figures in the data you used.

Multiplication/division When you multiply or divide numbers, report the answer with the same number of significant figures as the measured number with the *fewest* significant figures. See Sample Problem 2.

From *Essential Laboratory Manual for Chemistry: An Introduction to General, Organic, and Biological Chemistry*, Ninth Edition, Karen C. Timberlake. Copyright © 2007 by Pearson Education, Inc. Published by Benjamin Cummings. All rights reserved.

Sample Problem 2

Solve: $\dfrac{0.025 \times 4.62}{3.44} =$

Solution:

On the calculator, the steps are

$0.025 \times 4.62 \div 3.44 \quad = 0.033575581 \quad$ *calculator display*

$\qquad\qquad\qquad\qquad\quad = 0.034 \qquad\quad$ *final answer rounded to two significant figures*

Addition/subtraction When you add or subtract numbers, the reported answer has the same number of decimal places as the measured number with the *fewest* decimal places. See Sample Problem 3.

Sample Problem 3

Add: $2.11 + 104.056 + 0.1205$

Solution: $\qquad$ 2.11 $\quad$ *two decimal places*

$\qquad\qquad\quad$ 104.056

$\qquad\qquad\quad\underline{\quad 0.1205}$

$\qquad\qquad\quad$ 106.2865 $\;$ *calculator display*

$\qquad\qquad\quad$ 106.29 $\quad$ *final answer rounded to two decimal places*

C. Conversion Factors for Length

Metric factors If a quantity is expressed in two different metric units, a *metric equality* can be stated. For example, the length of 1 meter is the same as 100 cm, which gives the *equality* 1 m = 100 cm. When the values in the equality are written as a fraction, the ratio is called a *conversion factor*. Two fractions are always possible, and both are conversion factors for the equality.

$\qquad$ ***Equality*** $\qquad\qquad\qquad\qquad$ ***Conversion Factors***

$\qquad$ 1 m = 100 cm $\qquad\qquad\qquad \dfrac{100 \text{ cm}}{1 \text{ m}} \;$ and $\; \dfrac{1 \text{ m}}{100 \text{ cm}}$

Metric–U.S. system factors When a quantity measured in a metric unit is compared to its measured quantity in a U.S. unit, a *metric–U.S.* conversion factor can be written. For example, 1 inch is the same length as 2.54 cm, as seen in Figure 1.

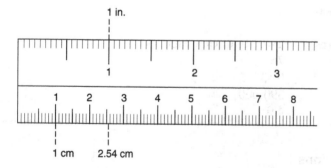

Figure 1 Comparing centimeters and inches

For the length of 1 inch, two conversion factors can be written.

$\qquad$ ***Equality*** $\qquad\qquad\qquad\qquad$ ***Conversion Factors***

$\qquad$ 1 in. = 2.54 cm $\qquad\qquad\qquad \dfrac{2.54 \text{ cm}}{1 \text{ in.}} \;$ and $\; \dfrac{1 \text{ in.}}{2.54 \text{ cm}}$

D. Conversion Factors for Volume

In the metric system, equalities for volume can be written along with their corresponding conversion factors. A useful metric–U.S. equality is the relationship of 1 quart equaling 946 mL.

Equality	*Conversion Factors*
1 L = 1000 mL	$\dfrac{1000\ \text{mL}}{1\ \text{L}}$ and $\dfrac{1\ \text{L}}{1000\ \text{mL}}$
1 qt = 946 mL	$\dfrac{946\ \text{mL}}{1\ \text{qt}}$ and $\dfrac{1\ \text{qt}}{946\ \text{mL}}$

E. Conversion Factors for Mass

In the metric system, equalities for mass can be written along with their corresponding conversion factors. A useful metric–U.S. equality is the relationship of 454 g equaling 1 pound.

Equality	*Conversion Factors*
1 kg = 1000 g	$\dfrac{1000\ \text{g}}{1\ \text{kg}}$ and $\dfrac{1\ \text{kg}}{1000\ \text{g}}$
1 lb = 454 g	$\dfrac{454\ \text{g}}{1\ \text{lb}}$ and $\dfrac{1\ \text{lb}}{454\ \text{g}}$

F. Measuring Temperature

Temperature measures the intensity of heat in a substance. A substance with little heat feels cold. Where the heat intensity is great, a substance feels hot. The temperature of our bodies is an indication of the heat produced. An infection may cause body temperature to deviate from normal. On the Celsius scale, water freezes at 0°C; on the Fahrenheit scale, water freezes at 32°F. A Celsius temperature is converted to its corresponding Fahrenheit temperature by using the following equation:

$$T_F = 1.8\ (T_C) + 32$$

When the Fahrenheit temperature is known, the Celsius temperature is determined by rearranging the equation. Be sure you subtract 32 from the T_F, then divide by 1.8.

$$T_C = \frac{(T_F) - 32}{1.8}$$

A Celsius temperature can be converted to a Kelvin temperature by using the following equation:

$$T_K = T_C + 273$$

Lab Information

Time:	2 hr
Comments:	Tear out the report sheets and place them beside the procedures.
	Determine what the smallest lines of measurement are on each measuring tool you use.
	Include an estimated digit for each measurement.
	Round off the calculator answers to the correct number of significant figures.
Related Topics:	Conversion factors, significant figures in mathematical operations, calculator use

Experimental Procedures

A. Rounding Off

Materials: Meterstick, solid

A.1 **Rounding** A student has rounded off some numbers. Determine whether the rounding was done correctly. If it is not correct, write the correctly rounded number.

A.2 **Area** Determine the length (cm) and width (cm) of the sides of the rectangle on the report sheet. Obtain a second set of measurements from another student. Record. Calculate the area (cm^2) of the rectangle using your measurements and this formula: Area = L × W. Obtain the area calculated by the other student. Compare the calculated areas from both sets of measurements.

A.3 **Volume of a solid by direct measurement** Obtain a solid object that has a regular shape, such as a cube, rectangular solid, or cylinder. Record its shape. Use a ruler to determine the dimensions of the solid in centimeters (cm). Use the appropriate formula from the following list to calculate the volume in cm^3.

Shape	Dimensions to Measure	Formulas for Volume
Cube	Length (L)	$V = L^3$
Rectangular solid	Length (L), width (W), height (H)	$V = L \times W \times H$
Cylinder	Diameter (D), height (H)	$V = \dfrac{\pi D^2 H}{4} = \dfrac{3.14 D^2 H}{4}$

B. Significant Figures in Calculations

B.1 Solve the multiplication and division problems. Report your answers with the correct number of significant figures.

B.2 Solve the addition and subtraction problems. Report your answers with the correct number of significant figures.

C. Conversion Factors for Length

Materials: Meterstick

C.1 **Metric factors** Observe the markings for millimeters on a meterstick. Write an equality that states the number of millimeters in 1 meter. Write two metric conversion factors for the relationship. Observe the number of millimeters in a centimeter. Write equality and corresponding conversion factors for the relationship between centimeters and millimeters.

C.2 **Metric–U.S. system factors** Measure the length of the dark line on the report sheet in centimeters and in inches. Convert any fraction to a decimal number. Divide the number of centimeters by the number of inches to give a relationship. Round off correctly for your reported answer. This is your *experimental* value for the number of centimeters in 1 inch.

C.3 **Your metric height** Record your height in inches. Or use a yardstick to measure. Using the appropriate conversion factors, *calculate* your height in centimeters and meters. Show your setup for each calculation.

$$\text{Height (in.)} \times \frac{2.54\ \text{cm}}{1\ \text{in.}} = \text{your height (cm)}$$

$$\text{Height (cm)} \times \frac{1\ \text{m}}{100\ \text{cm}} = \text{your height (m)}$$

D. Conversion Factors for Volume

Materials: 1-L graduated cylinder, 1-quart measure (or two 1-pint measures)

D.1 Observe the markings on a 1-liter graduated cylinder. Write an equality that states the number of milliliters in 1 liter. Write two conversion factors for the equality.

D.2 Using a 1-pint or 1-quart measure, transfer 1 quart of water to a 1-liter graduated cylinder. Record the number of milliliters in 1 quart. Write the equality that states the number of milliliters in a quart. Write two conversion factors for the equality.

E. Conversion Factors for Mass

Materials: Commercial product with mass (weight) of contents given on label

E.1 **Grams and pounds** Labels on commercial products list the amount of the contents in both metric and U.S. units. Obtain a commercial product. Record the mass (weight) of the contents stated on the product label. *Do **not** weigh.* If the weight is given in ounces, convert it to pounds (1 lb = 16 oz).

$$\underline{\hspace{2cm}}\ \text{oz} \times \frac{1\ \text{lb}}{16\ \text{oz}} = \underline{\hspace{2cm}}\ \text{lb}$$

Divide the grams of the product by its weight in pounds. (Be sure to use the correct number of significant figures.) This is your value for grams in one pound (g/lb).

E.2 **Pounds and kilograms** State the mass on the label in kilograms. If necessary, convert the number of grams to kilograms.

$$\underline{\hspace{2cm}}\ \text{g} \times \frac{1\ \text{kg}}{1000\ \text{g}} = \underline{\hspace{2cm}}\ \text{kg}$$

Divide the number of pounds by the number of kilograms. Report the ratio as lb/kg. (Be sure to use the correct number of significant figures.)

F. Measuring Temperature

Materials: Thermometer (°C), a 150- or 250-mL beaker, ice, and rock salt

F.1 Observe the markings on a thermometer. Indicate the lowest and highest temperatures that can be read using that thermometer. ***Caution: Never shake down a laboratory thermometer. Shaking a laboratory thermometer can cause breakage and serious accidents.***

F.2 To measure the temperature of a liquid, place the bulb of the thermometer in the center of the solution. Keep it *immersed* while you read the temperature scale. When the temperature becomes constant, record the temperature (°C). On most thermometers, you can estimate the tenths of a degree (0.1°C). A set of beakers with the following contents may be set up in the lab; otherwise fill the beakers as instructed. Determine the temperature of each of the following:

a. Room temperature: Place the thermometer on the lab bench.

b. Tap water: Fill a 250-mL beaker about 1/3 full of water.

c. Ice-water mixture: Add enough ice to the water in part b to double (approximately) the volume. Allow 5 minutes for the temperature to change.

d. A salted ice mixture: Add rock salt to the ice-water mixture in part c. Stir and allow a few minutes for the temperature to change.

F.3 Convert the Celsius temperatures to corresponding temperatures on the Fahrenheit and Kelvin scales.

Report Sheet

Date _____   Name _____

Section _____   Team _____

Instructor _____   _____

Pre-Lab Study Questions

1. What are the rules for rounding off numbers?

2. How do you determine how many digits to keep in an answer obtained by multiplying or dividing?

3. How is the number of significant figures determined for an answer obtained by adding or subtracting?

4. How is an equality used to write a conversion factor?

5. Is a body temperature of 39.4°C a normal temperature or does it indicate a fever?

A. Rounding Off

A.1 **Rounding** A student rounded off the following calculator displays to three significant figures. Indicate if the rounded number is correct. If it is incorrect, round off the display value properly.

Calculator Display	Student's Rounded Value	Correct (yes/no)	Corrected (if needed)
24.4704	24.5	_____	_____
143.63212	144	_____	_____
532 800	530	_____	_____
0.00858345	0.009	_____	_____
8	8.00	_____	_____

Report Sheet

A.2 Area

	Your measurements	**Another student's measurements**
Length =	_____	_____
Width =	_____	_____
Area =	_____	_____

(*Show calculations.*)

Why could two students obtain different values for the calculated areas of the same rectangle?

A.3 **Volume of a solid by direct measurement**

Shape of solid _____

Formula for volume of solid _____

Height _____   **Length** _____

Width _____   **Diameter** (*if cylinder*) _____

Volume of the solid _____
(*Show calculations of volume including the units.*)

Report Sheet

B. Significant Figures in Calculations

B.1 Perform the following multiplication and division calculations. Give a final answer with the correct number of significant figures:

4.5×0.28 _____

$0.1184 \times 8.00 \times 0.0345$ _____

$\dfrac{(42.4)(15.6)}{1.265}$ _____

$\dfrac{(35.56)(1.45)}{(4.8)(0.56)}$ _____

B.2 Perform the following addition and subtraction calculations. Give a final answer with the correct number of significant figures.

$13.45 \text{ mL} + 0.4552 \text{ mL}$ _____

$145.5 \text{ m} + 86.58 \text{ m} + 1045 \text{ m}$ _____

$1315 + 200 + 1100$ _____

$245.625 \text{ g} - 80.2 \text{ g}$ _____

$4.62 \text{ cm} - 0.885 \text{ cm}$ _____

Questions and Problems

Q.1 What is the combined mass in grams of objects that have masses of 0.2000 kg, 80.0 g, and 524 mg?

Q.2 A beaker has a mass of 225.08 g. When a liquid is added to the beaker, the combined mass is 238.254 g. What is the mass in grams of the liquid?

Report Sheet

C.   Conversion Factors for Length

C.1   **Metric factors**

Equality: 1 m   = _____ mm

Conversion factors: $\dfrac{\boxed{}\ \text{m}}{\boxed{}\ \text{mm}}$ and $\dfrac{\boxed{}\ \text{mm}}{\boxed{}\ \text{m}}$

Equality: 1 cm   = _____ mm

Conversion factors: $\dfrac{\boxed{}\ \text{cm}}{\boxed{}\ \text{mm}}$ and $\dfrac{\boxed{}\ \text{mm}}{\boxed{}\ \text{cm}}$

C.2   **Metric–U.S. system factors**

Line length (*measured*)   _____ in.

_____ cm

$\dfrac{\boxed{}\ \text{cm}}{\boxed{}\ \text{in.}}$ = $\dfrac{\boxed{}\ \text{cm}}{1 \text{ in.}}$ (*Experimental ratio*)

How close is your *experimental ratio* to the standard conversion factor of 2.54 cm/in.?

Report Sheet

C.3 **Your metric height**

Height (inches) _____
Height in centimeters (*calculated*)

_____in. × _____cm = _____cm
                                    1 in.

What is your height in meters?   _____m
(*Show your calculations here.*)

Questions and Problems (*Show complete setups.*)

Q.3 A pencil is 16.2 cm long. What is its length in millimeters (mm)?

Q.4 A roll of tape measures 45.5 inches. What is the length of the tape in meters?

D. Conversion Factors for Volume

D.1 Equality: 1 L = _____ mL

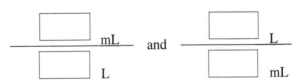

Conversion factors: [ ] mL / [ ] L   and   [ ] L / [ ] mL

D.2 Volume (mL) of 1 quart of water: _____ mL

Number of milliliters in 1 quart: _____ mL/qt (*experimental*)

Equality: 1 qt = _____ mL

Conversion factors: [ ] qt / [ ] mL   and   [ ] mL / [ ] qt

31

Report Sheet

Questions and Problems (*Show complete setups.*)

Q.5   A patient received 825 mL of fluid in one day. What is that volume in liters?

Q.6   How many liters of plasma are present in 8.5 pints? (1 qt = 2 pt)

E.   Conversion Factors for Mass

E.1   **Grams and pounds**

Name of commercial product   _____

Mass in grams stated on label   _____

Weight in lb or oz given on label   _____

Weight in lb   _____
(*Convert oz to lb if needed.*)

$$\frac{\text{Number of grams}}{\text{Number of lb}} = \frac{\boxed{} \text{ g}}{\boxed{} \text{ lb}} = \frac{\boxed{} \text{ g}}{1 \text{ lb}}$$

How does your experimental factor compare to the standard value of 454 g/lb?

E.2   **Pounds and kilograms**

Mass in kilograms (from label)   _____

Weight in lb   _____

$$\frac{\text{Number of lb}}{\text{Number of kg}} = \frac{\boxed{} \text{ lb}}{\boxed{} \text{ kg}} = \frac{\boxed{} \text{ lb}}{1 \text{ kg}}$$

How does your *experimental factor* compare to the standard value of 2.20 lb/kg?

Questions and Problems

Q.7   An infant has a mass of 3.40 kg. What is the weight of the infant in pounds?

Report Sheet

F. Measuring Temperature

F.1 Temperature scale(s) on the laboratory thermometer _____

Lowest temperature _____ Highest temperature _____

F.2	°C	(A.3) °F	K
a. Room temperature	_____	_____	_____
b. Tap water	_____	_____	_____
c. Ice-water mixture	_____	_____	_____
d. Salt ice-water mixture	_____	_____	_____

Questions and Problems

Q.8 Write an equation for each of the following temperature conversions:

a. °C to °F

b. °F to °C

c. °C to K

Q.9 A recipe calls for a baking temperature of 205°C. What temperature in °F should be set on the oven?

Density and Specific Gravity

Goals

- Calculate the density of a substance from measurements of its mass and volume.
- Calculate the specific gravity of a liquid from its density.
- Determine the specific gravity of a liquid using a hydrometer.

Discussion

A. Density of a Solid

To determine the density of a substance, you need to measure both its mass and its volume. You have carried out both of these procedures in previous labs. From the mass and volume, the density is calculated. If the mass is measured in grams and the volume in milliliters, the density will have the units of g/mL.

$$\text{Density of a substance} = \frac{\text{Mass of substance}}{\text{Volume of substance}} = \frac{\text{g of substance}}{\text{mL of substance}}$$

B. Density of a Liquid

To determine the density of a liquid, you need the mass and volume of the liquid. The mass of a liquid is determined by weighing. The mass of a container is obtained and then a certain volume of liquid is added and the combined mass determined. Subtracting the mass of the container gives the mass of the liquid. From the mass and volume, the density is calculated.

$$\text{Density of liquid} = \frac{\text{Mass (g) of liquid}}{\text{Volume (mL) of liquid}}$$

C. Specific Gravity

The specific gravity of a liquid is a comparison of the density of that liquid with the density of water, which is 1.00 g/mL (4°C).

$$\text{Specific gravity (sp gr)} = \frac{\text{Density of liquid (g/mL)}}{\text{Density of water (1.00 g/mL)}}$$

Specific gravity is a number with no units; the units of density (g/mL) have canceled out. This is one of the few measurements in chemistry written without any units.

From *Essential Laboratory Manual for Chemistry: An Introduction to General, Organic, and Biological Chemistry*, Ninth Edition, Karen C. Timberlake. Copyright © 2007 by Pearson Education, Inc. Published by Benjamin Cummings. All rights reserved.

Using a hydrometer The specific gravity of a fluid is determined by using a hydrometer. Small hydrometers (urinometers) are used in the hospital to determine the specific gravity of urine. Another type of hydrometer is used to measure the specific gravity of the fluid in your car battery. A hydrometer placed in a liquid is spun slowly to keep it from sticking to the sides of the container. The scale on the hydrometer is read at the lowest (center) point of the meniscus of the fluid. Read the specific gravity on the hydrometer to 0.001. See Figure 1.

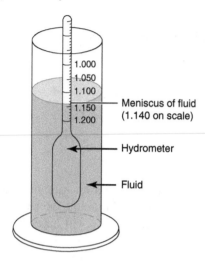

1.000
1.050
1.100
1.150
1.200

Meniscus of fluid
(1.140 on scale)

Hydrometer

Fluid

Figure 1 Measuring specific gravity using a hydrometer

Lab Information

Time: 2 hr

Comments: Tear out the report sheets and place them beside the procedures.
               Round off the calculator answers to the correct number of significant figures.
               Dispose of liquids properly as directed by your instructor.

Related Topics: Mass, volume, prefixes, significant figures, density, specific gravity

Experimental Procedures   *GOGGLES REQUIRED!*

A. Density of a Solid

Materials: Metal object, string or thread, graduated cylinder

A.1 **Mass of the solid** Obtain a solid metal object. Determine its mass and record.

A.2 **Volume of the solid by displacement** Obtain a graduated cylinder that is large enough to hold the solid metal object. Add water until the cylinder is about half full. Read the water level carefully and record. If the solid object is heavy, lower it into the water by attaching a string or thread. While the solid object is submerged in the water, record the final water level. Calculate the volume of the solid.

Volume of solid = Final water level − initial water level

A.3 **Calculating the density of the solid** Calculate the density (g/mL) of the solid by dividing its mass (g) by its volume (mL). Be sure to determine the correct number of significant figures in your calculated density value.

$$\text{Density of solid} = \frac{\text{Mass (g) of solid}}{\text{Volume (mL) of solid}}$$

A.4 If your instructor indicates that the solid is made of one of the substances in Table 1, use the density you calculated in A.3 to identify the metal from the known values for density.

Table 1 *Density Values of Some Metals*

Substance	Density (g/mL)
Aluminum	2.70
Brass	8.4
Copper	8.89
Iron	7.86
Lead	11.4
Nickel	8.85
Tin	7.18
Zinc	7.19

B. Density of a Liquid

Materials: 50-mL graduated cylinder, two liquid samples, 100-mL or 250-mL beaker

B.1 **Volume of liquid** Place about 20 mL of water in a 50-mL graduated cylinder. Record. (*Do not use the markings on beakers to measure volume; they are not precise.*)

B.2 **Mass of liquid** The mass of a liquid is found by weighing by difference. First, determine the mass of a small, dry beaker. Pour the liquid into the beaker, and reweigh. Record the combined mass. *Be sure to write down all the figures in the measurements.* Calculate the mass of the liquid.

> ***Taring a container on an electronic balance:*** The mass of a container on an electronic balance can be set to 0 by pressing the *tare* bar. As a substance is added to the container, the mass shown on the readout is for the *substance* only. (When a container is *tared,* it is not necessary to subtract the mass of the beaker.)

B.3 **Density of liquid** Calculate the density of the liquid by dividing its mass (g) by the volume (mL) of the liquid.

$$\text{Density of liquid} = \frac{\text{Mass (g) of liquid}}{\text{Volume (mL) of liquid}}$$

Repeat the same procedure for another liquid provided in the laboratory.

C. Specific Gravity

Materials: Water, liquids used in part B in graduated cylinders with hydrometers

C.1 Calculate the specific gravity (sp gr) of each liquid you used in B. Divide its density by the standard density of water (1.00 g/mL).

$$\text{Specific gravity} = \frac{\text{Density of a substance (g/mL)}}{\text{Density of water (1.00 g/mL)}}$$

C.2 Read the hydrometer set in a graduated cylinder containing the same liquid you used in the density section. Record. Some hydrometers use the European decimal point, which is a comma. The value 1,000 on a European scale is read as 1.000. Record specific gravity as a decimal number.

Report Sheet

Date _____   Name _____

Section _____   Team _____

Instructor _____   _____

Pre-Lab Study Questions

1. What property of oil makes it float on water?

2. Why would heating the gas in a hot air balloon make the balloon rise?

3. What is the difference between density and specific gravity?

A. Density of a Solid

A.1 **Mass of the solid**   _____

A.2 **Volume of the solid by displacement**

    Initial water level (mL)   _____

    Final water level with solid (mL)   _____

    Volume of solid (mL)   _____

A.3 **Calculating the density of the solid**   _____ g/mL
    (*Show calculations.*)

A.4 Type of metal   _____

Questions and Problems (*Show complete setups.*)

Q.1 An object made of aluminum has a mass of 8.37 g. When it was placed in a graduated cylinder containing 20.0 mL of water, the water level rose to 23.1 mL. Calculate the density and specific gravity of the object.

Report Sheet

B.   Density of a Liquid

	Liquid 1	**Liquid 2**
B.1 **Volume of liquid**		
Type of liquid	_____	_____
Volume (mL)	_____	_____
B.2 **Mass of liquid**		
Mass of beaker	_____	_____
Mass of beaker + liquid	_____	_____
Mass of liquid	_____	_____
B.3 **Density of liquid** Density (*Show calculations for density.*)	_____	_____

C.   Specific Gravity

C.1 Specific gravity (*Calculated using B.3*)	_____	_____
C.2 Specific gravity (*Hydrometer reading*)	_____	_____

How does the *calculated* specific gravity compare to the hydrometer reading for each liquid?

Questions and Problems (*Show complete setups.*)

Q.2   What is the mass of a solution that has a density of 0.775 g/mL and a volume of 50.0 mL?

Q.3   What is the volume of a solution that has a specific gravity of 1.2 and a mass of 185 g?

Atomic Structure and Electron Arrangement

Goals

- Write the correct symbols or names of some elements.
- Describe some physical properties of the elements you observe.
- Categorize an element as a metal or nonmetal from its physical properties.
- Given the complete symbol of an atom, determine its mass number, atomic number, and the number of protons, neutrons, and electrons.
- Describe the color of a flame produced by an element.
- Draw a model of an atom including the electron arrangement for the first 20 elements.

Discussion

Primary substances, called elements, build all the materials about you. More than 116 elements are known today. Some look similar, but others look unlike anything else. In this experiment, you will describe the physical properties of elements in a laboratory display and determine the location of elements on a blank periodic table.

A. Physical Properties of Elements

Metals are elements that are usually shiny or have a metallic luster. They are usually good conductors of heat and electricity, ductile (can be drawn into a wire), and malleable (can be molded into a shape). Some metals such as sodium or calcium may have a white coating of oxide formed by reacting with oxygen in the air. If these are cut, you can see the fresh shiny metal underneath. In contrast, nonmetals are not good conductors of heat and electricity, are brittle (not ductile), and appear dull, not shiny.

B. Periodic Table

The periodic table, shown on the inside front cover of this lab manual and your textbook, contains information about each of the elements. On the table, the horizontal rows are *periods,* and the vertical columns are *groups.* Each group contains elements that have similar physical and chemical properties. The groups are numbered across the top of the chart. Elements in Group 1A(1) are the *alkali metals,* elements in Group 2A(2) are the *alkaline earths,* and Group 7A(17) contains the *halogens.* Group 8A(18) contains the *noble gases,* which are elements that are not very reactive compared to other elements. A dark zigzag line that looks like a staircase separates the *metals* on the left side from the *nonmetals* on the right side.

C. Subatomic Particles

There are different kinds of atoms for each of the elements. Atoms are made up of smaller bits of matter called *subatomic particles. Protons* are positively charged particles, *electrons* are negatively charged, and *neutrons* are neutral (no charge). In an atom, the protons and neutrons are tightly packed in the tiny center called the *nucleus.* Most of the atom is empty space, which contains fast-moving electrons. Electrons are so small that their mass is considered to be negligible compared to the mass of the proton or neutron. The *atomic number* is equal to the number of protons. The *mass number* of an atom is the number of protons and neutrons.

$atomic\ number$ = number of protons (p^+)
$mass\ number$ = sum of the number of protons and neutrons $(p^+ + n^0)$

From *Essential Laboratory Manual for Chemistry: An Introduction to General, Organic, and Biological Chemistry*, Ninth Edition, Karen C. Timberlake. Copyright © 2007 by Pearson Education, Inc. Published by Benjamin Cummings. All rights reserved.

D. Isotopes

Isotopes are atoms of the same element that differ in the number of neutrons. This means that isotopes of an element have the same number of protons, but different mass numbers. The following example represents the symbol of a sulfur isotope that has 16 protons and 18 neutrons.

Complete Symbol of an Isotope

Meaning

mass number (p^+ and n^0) → **34**   This atom has 16 protons and 18 neutrons.

symbol of element → **S**   The element is sulfur.

atomic number (p^+) → **16**   The atom has 16 protons.

E. Flame Tests

The chemistry of an element strongly depends on the arrangement of the electrons. The energy levels for electrons of atoms of the *first 20 elements* have the following number of electrons.

Electron Arrangement for Elements 1–20
Level 1 ($2e^-$)   Level 2 ($8e^-$)   Level 3 ($8e^-$)   Level 4 ($2e^-$)

When electrons absorb specific amounts of energy, they can attain higher energy levels. In order to return to the lower, more stable energy levels, electrons release energy. If the energy released is the same amount as the energy that makes up visible light, the element produces a color.

When heated, many of the elements in Groups 1a and 2a produce colorful flames. Each element produces a characteristic color. When the light from one of these flames passes through a glass prism or crystal, a series of color lines appears. The spaces between lines appear dark. Such a series of lines, known as a *spectrum,* is used to identify elements in water, food, the sun, stars, and on other planets.

F. Drawing Models of Atoms

A model of an atom can be drawn to show the number of protons and neutrons in the nucleus with the electrons shown in energy shells. This is an oversimplification of the true nature of atoms, but the model does illustrate the relationship of the subatomic particles. By observing the electron arrangement, you can determine the number of valence electrons for the atoms of that element.

We can illustrate the model of an atom of boron with a mass number of 11. With an atomic number of 5, boron has 5 protons. To find the number of neutrons, the atomic number (number of protons) is subtracted from the mass number of 11 (for this isotope) to give 6 neutrons. Boron has 3 valence electrons, which puts boron in Group 3.

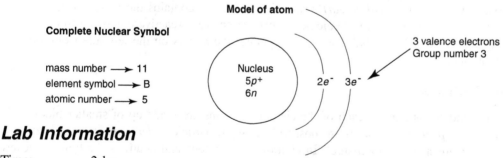

Lab Information

Time: 2 hr

Comments: Obtain a periodic table as a reference.
               Tear out the report sheets and place them beside the procedures.
               Carefully observe the physical properties of the elements in the display.

Related Topics: Names and symbols of the elements, periodic table, atoms, subatomic particles,
               isotopes, electrons and protons, energy levels, and electron arrangement

Experimental Procedures

A.   Physical Properties of Elements

Materials: A display of elements

Observe the elements in the laboratory display of elements. In the report sheet, write the symbol and atomic number for each element listed. Describe some physical properties such as color and luster. From your observations, identify each element as a metal (M) or a nonmetal (NM).

B.   Periodic Table

Materials: Periodic table, colored pencils, display of elements

B.1   On the incomplete periodic table provided in the report sheet, write the atomic numbers and symbols of the elements you observed in part A. Write the group number at the top of each column of elements. Write the period numbers for each of the horizontal rows shown. Using different colors, shade in the columns that contain the alkali metals, alkaline earths, halogens, and noble gases. With another color, shade in the transition elements. Draw a heavy line to separate the metals and nonmetals.

B.2   *Without looking* at the display of elements, use the periodic table to decide whether the elements listed on the report sheet would be metals or nonmetals; shiny or dull. *After* you complete your predictions, observe those same elements in the display to see if you predicted correctly.

C.   Subatomic Particles

For each of the neutral atoms described in the table, write the atomic number, mass number, and number of protons, neutrons, and electrons.

D.   Isotopes

Complete the information for each of the isotopes of calcium: the complete nuclear symbol and the number of protons, neutrons, and electrons.

E.   Flame Tests

Materials: Bunsen burner, spot plate, flame-test (nichrome) wire, cork,
         100-mL beaker, 1 M HCl, 0.1 M solutions (dropper bottles): $CaCl_2$, KCl, $BaCl_2$,
         $SrCl_2$, $CuCl_2$, NaCl, and unknown solutions

Obtain a spot plate, flame-test wire, and cork stopper. Bend one end of the flame-test wire into a small loop and secure the other end in a cork stopper. Pour a small amount of 1 M HCl into a 100-mL beaker. Rinse the spot plate in distilled water. Place 6–8 drops of each test solution in separate indentations of the spot plate. Label the spot plate diagram in the laboratory report to match the solutions. Be careful not to mix the different solutions.

<u>CAUTION</u> 1 M HCl is corrosive! Be careful when you use it. Wash off any HCl spills on the skin with tap water for 10 minutes.

Adjust the flame of a Bunsen burner until it is nearly colorless. Clean the test wire by dipping the loop in the HCl in the beaker and placing it in the flame of the Bunsen burner. If you see a strong color in the flame while heating the wire, dip it in the HCl again. Repeat until the color is gone.

Observing Flame Colors

Dip the cleaned wire in one of the solutions on the spot plate. Make sure that a thin film of the solution adheres to the loop. See Figure 1. Move the loop of the wire into the lower portion of the flame and record the color you observe. For each solution, it is the first element in the formula that is responsible for color.

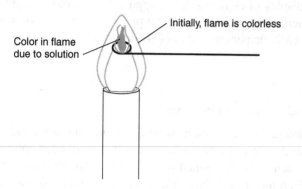

Color in flame due to solution

Initially, flame is colorless

Figure 1   Using a flame-test wire to test for flame color

Note: The color of potassium in the KCl flame is short-lived. Be sure to observe the color of the flame from the KCl solution within the first few seconds of heating. Repeat each flame test until you can describe the color of the flame produced. Clean the wire and repeat the flame test with the other solutions.

Identifying Solutions

Obtain unknown solutions as indicated by your instructor and record their code letters. Place 6–8 drops of each unknown solution in a clean spot plate. Use the flame-test procedure to determine the identity of the unknown solution. You may wish to recheck the flame color of the known solution that best matches the flame color of an unknown. For example, if you think your unknown is KCl, recheck the color of the KCl solution to confirm.

F.   Drawing Models of Atoms

Draw a model of each atom listed on the laboratory report. Indicate the number of valence electrons and the group number for the element.

Report Sheet

Date _____   Name _____

Section _____   Team _____

Instructor _____   _____

1. Describe the periodic table.

2. Where are the alkali metals and the halogens located on the periodic table?

3. On the following list of elements, circle the symbols of the transition elements and underline the symbols of the halogens:

    Mg   Cu   Br   Ag   Ni   Cl .   Fe   F

4. Complete the list of names of elements and symbols:

Name of Element	Symbol	Name of Element	Symbol
Potassium			Na
Sulfur			P
Nitrogen			Fe
Magnesium			Cl
Copper			Ag

Report Sheet

A. Physical Properties of Elements

Element	Symbol	Atomic Number	Physical Properties		
			Color	Luster	Metal/Nonmetal
Aluminum	_____	_____	_____	_____	_____
Carbon	_____	_____	_____	_____	_____
Copper	_____	_____	_____	_____	_____
Iron	_____	_____	_____	_____	_____
Magnesium	_____	_____	_____	_____	_____
Nickel	_____	_____	_____	_____	_____
Nitrogen	_____	_____	_____	_____	_____
Oxygen	_____	_____	_____	_____	_____
Phosphorus	_____	_____	_____	_____	_____
Silicon	_____	_____	_____	_____	_____
Silver	_____	_____	_____	_____	_____
Sulfur	_____	_____	_____	_____	_____
Tin	_____	_____	_____	_____	_____
Zinc	_____	_____	_____	_____	_____

Report Sheet

B. Periodic Table

B.1

Questions and Problems

Q.1 From their positions on the periodic table, categorize the following elements as metals (M) or nonmetals (NM).

Na _____ S _____ Cu _____ F _____ Fe _____ C _____ Ca _____

Q.2 Give the name of each of the following elements:

a. Noble gas in Period 2 _____ b. Halogen in Period 2 _____

c. Alkali metal in Period 3 _____ d. Halogen in Period 3 _____

e. Alkali metal in Period 4 _____

Report Sheet

B.2

Element	Metal/Nonmetal	Prediction: Shiny or Dull	Correct? Yes/No
Chromium			
Gold			
Lead			
Cadmium			
Silicon			

C. Subatomic Particles

Element	Atomic Number	Mass Number	Protons	Neutrons	Electrons
Iron				30	
		27			13
			19	20	
Bromine		80			
Gold		197			
			53	74	

D. Isotopes

Nuclear Symbol	Protons	Neutrons	Electrons
$^{40}_{20}Ca$			
	20	22	
$^{43}_{20}Ca$			
		24	20
$^{46}_{20}Ca$			

Report Sheet

Questions and Problems

Q.3   A neutral atom has a mass number of 80 and has 45 neutrons. Write its complete symbol.

Q.4   An atom has two more protons and two more electrons than the atom in question 3. What is its complete symbol?

E.   Flame Tests

Spot plate diagram

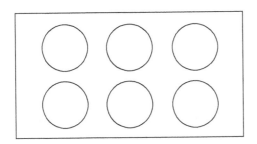

Solution	Element	Color of Flame
$CaCl_2$	Ca	_____
KCl	K	_____
$BaCl_2$	Ba	_____
$SrCl_2$	Sr	_____
$CuCl_2$	Cu	_____
NaCl	Na	_____

Unknown Solution(s)
Identification letter   ☐   ☐   ☐

Color of flame   _____   _____   _____

Element present   _____   _____   _____

Questions and Problems

Q.5   You are cooking spaghetti in water you have salted with NaCl. You notice that when the water boils over, it causes the flame of the gas burner to turn bright orange. How would you explain the appearance of a color in the flame?

Report Sheet

F. Drawing Models of Atoms

Atom	Model of Atom	Number of Valence Electrons	Group Number
$^{7}_{3}$Li			
$^{14}_{7}$N			
$^{25}_{12}$Mg			
$^{27}_{13}$Al			
$^{37}_{17}$Cl			
$^{34}_{16}$S			

Questions and Problems

Q.6 Write the electron arrangement for the following elements:

Energy Level

Element	1	2	3	4
P				
Na				
F				
C				
Ca				

Compounds and Their Formulas

Goals

- Compare physical properties of a compound with the properties of the elements that formed it.
- Identify a compound as ionic or covalent.
- Determine the subscripts in the formula of a compound.
- Write the electron-dot structure for an atom and an ion.
- Write a correct formula and name of an ionic or covalent compound.
- Write a correct formula and name of a compound containing a polyatomic ion.

Discussion

Nearly everything is made of compounds. A compound consists of two or more different elements that are chemically combined. Most atoms form compounds by forming octets in their outer shells. The attractions between the atoms are called *chemical bonds*. For example, when a metal combines with a nonmetal, the metal loses electrons to form a positive ion and the nonmetal gains electrons to form a negative ion. The attraction between the positive ions and the negative ions is called an *ionic bond*. When two nonmetals form a compound, they share electrons and form *covalent bonds*. In covalent compounds, the atoms are bonded as individual units called *molecules*. See Table 1.

Table 1 *Types of Bonding in Compounds*

Compound	Types of Elements	Characteristics	Type of Bonding
NaCl	Metal, nonmetal	Ions (Na^+, Cl^-)	Ionic
$MgBr_2$	Metal, nonmetal	Ions (Mg^{2+}, Br^-)	Ionic
CCl_4	Two nonmetals	Molecules	Covalent
NH_3	Two nonmetals	Molecules	Covalent

In a compound, there is a definite proportion of each element. This is represented in the formula, which gives the lowest whole number ratio of each kind of atom. For example, water has the formula H_2O. This means that two atoms of hydrogen and one atom of oxygen are combined in every molecule of water. Water never has any other formula.

When we observe a compound or an element, we see physical properties such as color and luster. We measure other physical properties such as density, melting point, and boiling point. When elements undergo chemical combination, the physical properties change to the physical properties of the new substances that form. For example, when silver tarnishes, the physical property of the shiny, silver metal changes to the dull, gray color as silver combines with sulfur to form tarnish, Ag_2S. A chemical change has occurred when the reaction between elements causes a change in their physical properties.

A. Electron-Dot Structures

When atoms of metals in Groups 1A(1), 2A(2), or 3A(13) react with atoms of nonmetals in Groups 5A(15), 6A(16), or 7A(17), the metals lose electrons and the nonmetals gain electrons in their valence shells. We can predict the number of electrons lost or gained by analyzing the electron-dot structures of the atoms. In an electron-dot structure, the valence electrons are represented as dots around the symbol of the atom. For example, calcium, electron arrangement 2-8-8-2, has two valence electrons

From *Essential Laboratory Manual for Chemistry: An Introduction to General, Organic, and Biological Chemistry*, Ninth Edition, Karen C. Timberlake. Copyright © 2007 by Pearson Education, Inc. Published by Benjamin Cummings. All rights reserved.

and an electron-dot structure with two dots. Chlorine, electron arrangement 2-8-7, has seven valence electrons and an electron-dot structure with seven dots.

$$\text{Ca} \cdot \qquad : \overset{\cdot\cdot}{\underset{\cdot\cdot}{\text{Cl}}} \cdot$$

Ca loses two electrons to attain an octet. This gives it an ionic charge of 2+. It is now a calcium ion with an electron arrangement of 2-8-8. As a positive ion, it keeps the same name as the element.

	Calcium Atom, Ca	**Calcium Ion, Ca^{2+}**	
Electron arrangement	2-8-8-2	2-8-8	(Two electrons lost)
Number of protons	$20p^+$	$20p^+$	(Same)
Number of electrons	$20e^-$	$18e^-$	(Two fewer electrons)
Net ionic charge	0	2+	

When nonmetals (5, 6, or 7 valence electrons) combine with metals, they gain electrons to become stable, and form negatively charged ions. For example, a chlorine atom gains one valence electron to become stable with an electron arrangement of 2-8-8. With the addition of one electron, chlorine becomes a chloride ion with an ionic charge of 1–. In the name of a binary compound with two different elements, the name of the negative ion ends in *ide*.

	Chlorine Atom, Cl	**Chloride Ion, Cl^-**	
Electron arrangement	2-8-7	2-8-8	(Electron added)
Number of protons	$17p^+$	$17p^+$	(Same)
Number of electrons	$17e^-$	$18e^-$	(One more electron)
Net ionic charge	0	1–	

B. Ionic Compounds and Formulas

The group number on the periodic table can be used to determine the ionic charges of elements in each family of elements. *Nonmetals form ions when they combine with a metal.*

Group number	1A(1)	2A(2)	3A(13)	4A(14)	5A(15)	6A(16)	7A(17)	8A(18)
Valence electrons	$1e^-$	$2e^-$	$3e^-$	$4e^-$	$5e^-$	$6e^-$	$7e^-$	$8e^-$
Electron change	lose 1	lose 2	lose 3	none	gain 3	gain 2	gain 1	no change
Ionic charge	1+	2+	3+	none	3–	2–	1–	none

In an ionic formula, the *number of electrons lost is equal to the number of electrons gained*. The overall net charge is zero. To balance the charge, we must determine the smallest number of positive and negative ions that give an overall charge of zero (0). We can illustrate the process by representing the ions Ca^{2+} and Cl^- as geometric shapes.

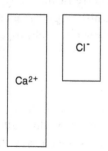

The charge is balanced by using two Cl^- ions to match the charge of the Ca^{2+} ion. The number of ions needed gives the subscripts in the formula for the compound $CaCl_2$. (The subscript 1 for Ca is understood.) In any ionic formula, *only the symbols are written, not their ionic charges.*

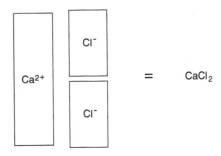

C.   Ionic Compounds with Transition Metals

Most of the transition metals can form more than one kind of positive ion. We will illustrate variable valence with iron. Iron forms two ions, one (Fe^{2+}) with a 2+ charge, and another (Fe^{3+}) with a 3+ charge. To distinguish between the two ions, a Roman numeral that gives the ionic charge of that particular ion follows the element name. The Roman numeral is always included in the names of compounds with variable positive ions. In an older naming system, the ending *ous* indicates the lower valence; the ending *ic* indicates the higher one. See Table 2.

Table 2 *Some Ions of the Transition Elements*

Ion	Names	Compound	Names
Fe^{2+}	Iron(II) ion	$FeCl_2$	Iron(II) chloride
Fe^{3+}	Iron(III) ion	$FeCl_3$	Iron(III) chloride
Cu^+	Copper(I) ion	$CuCl$	Copper(I) chloride
Cu^{2+}	Copper(II) ion	$CuCl_2$	Copper(II) chloride

Among the transition metals, a few elements (zinc, silver, and cadmium) form only a single type of ion; they have a fixed ionic charge. Thus, they are *not* variable and *do not need* a Roman numeral in their names.

Zn^{2+} zinc ion Ag^+ silver ion Cd^{2+} cadmium ion

D.   Ionic Compounds with Polyatomic Ions

A compound that consists of three or more kinds of atoms will contain a *polyatomic ion*. A polyatomic ion is a group of atoms with an overall charge. That charge, which is usually negative, is the result of adding electrons to a group of atoms to complete octets. The most common polyatomic ions consist of the nonmetals C, N, S, P, Cl, or Br combined with two to four oxygen atoms. Some examples are given in Table 3. The ions are named by replacing the ending of the nonmetal with *ate* or *ite*. The *ite* ending has one oxygen less than the most common form of the ion, which has an *ate* ending. Ammonium ion, NH_4^+, is positive because its group of atoms lost one electron.

Table 3 *Some Polyatomic Ions*

Common Polyatomic Ion	One Oxygen Less
NH_4^+ ammonium ion	
OH^- hydroxide ion	
NO_3^- nitrate ion	NO_2^- nitrite ion
CO_3^{2-} carbonate ion	
HCO_3^- bicarbonate ion (hydrogen carbonate ion)	
SO_4^{2-} sulfate ion	SO_3^{2-} sulfite ion
HSO_4^- bisulfate ion (hydrogen sulfate ion)	HSO_3^- bisulfite ion (hydrogen sulfite ion)
PO_4^{3-} phosphate ion	PO_3^{3-} phosphite ion

To write a formula with a polyatomic ion, we determine the ions needed for charge balance just as we did with the simple ions. When two or more polyatomic ions are needed, the formula of the ion is enclosed in parentheses and the subscript placed *outside*. *No change is ever made in the formula of the polyatomic ion itself.* Consider the formula of the compound formed by Ca^{2+} and NO_3^- ions.

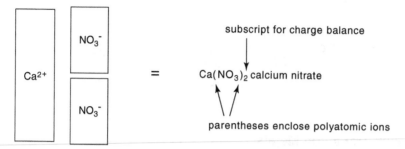

E. Covalent (Molecular) Compounds

Covalent bonds form between two nonmetals found in Groups 4A(14), 5A(15), 6A(16), or 7A(17) or H. In a *covalent compound,* octets are achieved by sharing electrons between atoms. The sharing of one pair of electrons is called a single bond. A double bond is the sharing of two pairs of electrons between atoms. In a triple bond, three pairs of electrons are shared. To write the formula of a covalent compound, determine the number of electrons needed to complete an octet. For example, nitrogen in Group 5A(15) has five valence electrons. Nitrogen atoms need three more electrons for an octet; they share three electrons.

Electron-Dot Structures

The formulas of covalent compounds are determined by sharing the valence electrons until each atom has an octet. For example, in water (H_2O), oxygen shares two electrons with two hydrogen atoms. Oxygen has an octet and hydrogen is stable because it has two electrons in the first valence shell.

Dot Structure for H_2O

H   shared electrons
  ..
: O : H

H   single bonds
  |
O — H

In another example, we look at a compound, CO_2, that has double bonds. In the elements' electron-dot structures, carbon has 4 valence electrons and each oxygen atom has 6. Thus a total of 16 (4 + 6 + 6) electrons can be used in forming the octets by sharing electrons. We can use the following steps to determine the electron-dot structure for CO_2:

1. Connect the atoms with pairs of electrons, thus using 4 electrons.

    O :: C :: O

2. Place the remaining 12 electrons (16 – 4) around the atoms. Don't add more electrons.

    : O :: C :: O :

3. If octets *cannot* be completed, try sharing more electrons. In step 2, the octets are complete for the oxygen atoms, but not for the carbon. One pair of electrons from each oxygen atom is moved to share with carbon. Now all the atoms have octets. There are still 16 electrons used, but they are now arranged to give each atom an octet. There are two double bonds in the CO_2 molecule.

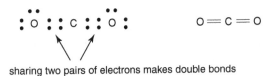

sharing two pairs of electrons makes double bonds

Names of Covalent Compounds

Binary (two-element) covalent compounds are named by using *prefixes* that give the number of atoms of each element in the compound. The first nonmetal is named by the element name; the second ends in *ide*. The prefixes are derived from the Greek names: mono (1), di (2), tri (3), tetra (4), penta (5), hexa (6), hepta (7), and octa (8). Usually the prefix *mono* is not shown for the first element. See Table 4.

Table 4 *Some Formulas and Names of Covalent Compounds*

Formula	Name
CO	carbon **mono**xide
CO_2	carbon **di**oxide
PCl_3	phosphorus **tri**chloride
N_2O_4	**di**nitrogen **tetr**oxide (drop *a* in a double vowel)
SCl_6	sulfur **hexa**chloride

Lab Information

Time: 2–3 hr

Comments: Tear out the report sheets and place them beside the matching procedures.

Related Topics: Ions, ionic bonds, naming ionic compounds, covalent bond, covalent compounds, naming covalent compounds

Experimental Procedures

A. Electron-Dot Structures

Write the electron arrangements for atoms and their ions. Determine the number of electrons lost or gained and write the electron-dot structure of the ion that each would form along with its symbol, ionic charge, and name.

B. Ionic Compounds and Formulas
Materials: Reference books: *Merck Index* or *CRC Handbook of Chemistry and Physics*

B.1 **Physical properties** In the laboratory display of compounds observe NaCl, sodium chloride. Describe its appearance. Using a chemistry reference such as the *Merck Index* or the *CRC Handbook of Chemistry and Physics,* record the density and melting point.

B.2 **Formulas of ionic compounds** Use the periodic table to write the positive and negative ion in each compound. Use charge balance (net total = zero) to write the correct formula. Use subscripts when two or more ions are needed.

B.3 **Names of ionic compounds** From the formula of each ionic compound, write the compound name by placing the metal name first, then the nonmetal name ending in *ide*.

C. Ionic Compounds with Transition Metals

C.1 **Physical properties** In the display of compounds observe $FeCl_3$, iron(III) chloride. Describe its appearance. Using a chemistry reference such as the *Merck Index* or the *CRC Handbook of Chemistry and Physics,* record the density and melting point.

C.2 **Formulas of ionic compounds** Use the periodic table to write the positive and negative ion in each compound. Use charge balance (net total = zero) to write the correct formula. Use subscripts when two or more ions are needed.

C.3 **Names of ionic compounds** From the formula of each ionic compound, write the compound name by placing the metal name first, then the nonmetal name ending in *ide.* Be sure to indicate the ionic charge if the transition metal has a variable valence by using a Roman numeral.

D. Ionic Compounds with Polyatomic Ions

D.1 **Physical properties** In the display of compounds observe K_2CO_3, potassium carbonate. Describe its appearance. Using a chemistry reference book such as the *Merck Index* or the *CRC Handbook of Chemistry and Physics,* record the density and melting point.

D.2 **Formulas of ionic compounds** Use the periodic table to write the positive and negative (polyatomic) ion in each compound. Use charge balance (net total = zero) to write the correct formula. Use subscripts when two or more ions are needed. Use parentheses when two or more polyatomic ions are needed for charge balance.

D.3 **Names of ionic compounds** Name the compounds listed, using the correct names of the polyatomic ions.

E. Covalent (Molecular) Compounds

E.1 **Electron-dot formulas of elements** Write the electron-dot structure for each nonmetal.

E.2 **Physical properties** In the display of compounds observe water, H_2O. Describe its appearance. Using a chemistry reference such as the *Merck Index* or the *CRC Handbook of Chemistry and Physics,* record the density and melting point.

E.3 **Electron-dot structures** Write the electron-dot structure for each covalent compound. Name each compound, using prefixes to indicate the number of atoms of each element. By convention, the prefix *mono* can be omitted from the name of the first nonmetal.

Report Sheet

Date _____   Name _____

Section _____   Team _____

Instructor _____   _____

Pre-Lab Study Questions

1. Where are the valence electrons in an atom?

2. Why do compounds of metals and nonmetals consist of ions?

3. How are positive and negative ions formed?

4. How do subscripts represent the charge balance of ions?

5. Why are electrons shared in covalent compounds?

6. How do the names of covalent compounds differ from the names of ionic compounds?

7. What are polyatomic ions?

Report Sheet

A. Electron-Dot Structures

Element	Atomic Number	Electron Arrangement of Atom	Electron-Dot Structure	Loss or Gain of Electrons	Electron Arrangement of Ion	Ionic Charge	Symbol of Ion	Name of Ion
Sodium	11	2-8-1	Na·	lose $1e^-$	2-8	1+	Na^+	sodium ion
Nitrogen	7	2-5	$\cdot \ddot{N} \cdot$	gain $3e^-$	2-8	3–	N^{3-}	nitride ion
Aluminum								
Chlorine								
Calcium								
Oxygen								

Report Sheet

B.   Ionic Compounds and Formulas

B.1   Physical properties

Compound	Appearance	Density	Melting Point

B.2   Formulas of ionic compounds

Name	Positive Ion	Negative Ion	Formula
Sodium chloride	Na^+	Cl^-	
Magnesium chloride			
Calcium oxide			
Lithium phosphide			
Aluminum sulfide			
Calcium nitride			

B.3   Names of ionic compounds

K_2S	Potassium sulfide
BaF_2	
MgO	
Na_3N	
$AlCl_3$	
Mg_3P_2	

Report Sheet

C. Ionic Compounds with Transition Metals

C.1 Physical properties

Compound	Appearance	Density	Melting Point

C.2 Formulas of ionic compounds

Name	Positive Ion	Negative Ion	Formula
Iron(III) chloride	Fe^{3+}	Cl^-	
Iron(II) oxide			
Copper(I) sulfide			
Copper(II) nitride			
Zinc oxide			
Silver sulfide			

C.3 Names of ionic compounds

Cu_2S	Copper(I) sulfide
Fe_2O_3	
$CuCl_2$	
FeS	
Ag_2O	
$FeBr_2$	

D. Ionic Compounds with Polyatomic Ions

D.1 Physical properties

Compound	Appearance	Density	Melting Point

Report Sheet

D.2 Formulas of ionic compounds

Name	Positive Ion	Negative Ion	Formula
Potassium carbonate	K^+	CO_3^{2-}	
Sodium nitrate			
Calcium bicarbonate			
Aluminum hydroxide			
Lithium phosphate			
Potassium sulfate			

D.3 Names of ionic compounds

$CaSO_4$	Calcium sulfate
$Al(NO_3)_3$	
Na_2CO_3	
$MgSO_3$	
$Cu(OH)_2$	
$Mg_3(PO_4)_2$	

Questions and Problems

Q.1 Write the correct formulas for the following ions:

sodium ion _____   oxide ion _____   calcium ion _____

chloride ion _____   sulfate ion _____   iron(II) ion _____

E.   Covalent (Molecular) Compounds

E.1   Electron-dot formulas of elements

Hydrogen	Carbon	Nitrogen	Oxygen	Sulfur	Chlorine
H •					

Compounds and Their Formulas

E.2 Physical properties

Compound	Appearance	Density	Melting Point

E.3 Electron-dot structures

Compound	Electron-Dot Structure	Name
H_2O		
SBr_2		
PCl_3		
CBr_4		
SO_3		

Questions and Problems

Q.2 a. Identify each of the following compounds as *ionic* or *covalent*.
    b. Write the correct formula for each.

	Ionic/Covalent	Formula
sodium oxide	_____	_____
iron(III) bromide	_____	_____
sodium carbonate	_____	_____
carbon tetrachloride	_____	_____
nitrogen tribromide	_____	_____

Chemical Reactions and Equations

Goals

- Observe physical and chemical properties associated with chemical changes.
- Give evidence for the occurrence of a chemical reaction.
- Write a balanced equation for a chemical reaction.
- Identify a reaction as a combination, decomposition, replacement, or combustion reaction.

Discussion

When a substance undergoes a physical change, it changes its appearance but not its composition. For example, when silver (Ag) melts and forms liquid silver (Ag), it undergoes a physical change from solid to liquid. In a chemical change, a substance is changed to give a new substance with a different composition and different properties. For example, when silver tarnishes, the shiny silver (Ag) changes to a dull-gray silver sulfide (Ag_2S), a new substance with different properties and a different composition. See Table 1.

Table 1 *Comparison of Physical and Chemical Changes*

Some Physical Changes	Some Chemical Changes
Change in state	Formation of a gas (bubbles)
Change in size	Formation of a solid (precipitates)
Tearing	Disappearance of a solid (dissolves)
Breaking	Change in color
Grinding	Heat is given off or absorbed

Balancing a Chemical Equation

In a chemical reaction, atoms in the reactants are rearranged to produce new combinations of atoms in the products. However, the total number of atoms of each element in the reactants is equal to the total number of atoms in the products. In an equation, the reactants are shown on the left and the products on the right. An arrow between them indicates that a chemical reaction takes place.

$$\text{Reactants} \longrightarrow \text{Products}$$

To balance the number of atoms of each element on the left and right sides of the arrow, we write a number called a *coefficient* in front of the formula containing that particular element. Consider the balancing of the following unbalanced equation. The state of the substances as gas is shown as (g).

$N_2(g) + H_2(g) \longrightarrow NH_3(g)$	*Unbalanced equation*
$N_2(g) + H_2(g) \longrightarrow \mathbf{2}NH_3(g)$	*A coefficient of 2 balances the N atoms.*
$N_2(g) + \mathbf{3}H_2(g) \longrightarrow \mathbf{2}NH_3(g)$	*A coefficient of 3 balances the H atoms.*
	The equation is now balanced.

From *Essential Laboratory Manual for Chemistry: An Introduction to General, Organic, and Biological Chemistry*, Ninth Edition, Karen C. Timberlake. Copyright © 2007 by Pearson Education, Inc. Published by Benjamin Cummings. All rights reserved.

Types of Reactions

There are many different chemical reactions, but most can be classified into the types of reactions shown in Table 2.

Table 2 *Common Types of Chemical Reactions*

Type of Reaction	Description	Example Equation
Combination	Elements or simple compounds form a more complex product.	$Cu + S \rightarrow CuS$
Decomposition	A reacting substance is split into simpler products.	$CaCO_3 \rightarrow CaO + CO_2$
Single replacement	One element takes the place of another element in a compound.	$Mg + 2HCl \rightarrow MgCl_2 + H_2$
Double replacement	Elements in two compounds switch places.	$AgNO_3 + NaCl \rightarrow AgCl + NaNO_3$
Combustion	Reactant and oxygen form an oxide product.	$S + O_2 \rightarrow SO_2$

Lab Information

Time:	2–2½ hr
Comments:	Read all the directions and safety instructions carefully.
	Match the labels on bottles and containers with the names of the substances you need.
	Label your containers with the formulas of the chemicals you place in them.
	Be sure that long hair is tied back.
	A Bunsen burner is a potential hazard. Keep your work area clear of books, papers, backpacks, and other potentially flammable items.
	Tear out the report sheets and place them beside the matching procedures.
Related Topics:	Chemical change, chemical equation, balancing chemical equations

Experimental Procedures

A. Magnesium and Oxygen

Wear your goggles!

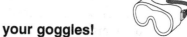

Materials: Magnesium ribbon (2–3 cm long), tongs, Bunsen burner

A.1 Obtain a small strip (2–3 cm) of magnesium ribbon. Record its appearance. Using a pair of tongs to hold the end of the magnesium ribbon, ignite it using the flame of a Bunsen burner. *As soon as the magnesium ribbon ignites, remove it from the flame. Shield your eyes as the ribbon burns.* Record your observations of the reaction and the physical properties of the product. Use complete sentences to describe your observations.

A.2 Balance the equation given for the reaction. Use 1 as a coefficient when one unit of that substance is required. The letters in parentheses indicate the physical state of the reactant or product: (*g*) gas, (*s*) solid. *Unbalanced equation:* $Mg(s)$ + $O_2(g)$ $MgO(s)$

A.3 Identify the type of reaction that has occurred. For this reaction, more than one reaction type may be used to classify the reaction.

B. Zinc and Copper(II) Sulfate

Materials: Two test tubes, test tube rack, 1 M CuSO$_4$ (copper(II) sulfate solution), Zn(s)

For all the experiments in parts B–E, use small quantities. For solids, use the amount of compound that will fit on the tip of a spatula or small scoop. Carefully pour small amounts of liquids into your own beakers and other containers. Measure out 3 mL of water in a test tube. Use this volume as a reference level for each of the experiments.

Do *not* place droppers or stirring rods into reagent bottles. They may contaminate a reagent for the entire class. Discard unused chemicals as indicated by your instructor.

B.1 Pour 3 mL (match the reference volume) of the *blue solution,* 1 M CuSO$_4$ (one molar copper(II) sulfate), into each of two test tubes. Obtain a small piece of zinc metal. Describe the appearance of the CuSO$_4$ solution and the small piece of zinc metal. Add the Zn metal piece to the CuSO$_4$ solution in one of the test tubes. The CuSO$_4$ solution in the other test tube is your reference for the initial solution color. Place the test tubes in your test tube rack and observe the color of the CuSO$_4$ solutions and the Zn piece again at 15 and 30 minutes. Pour the CuSO$_4$ solutions into the sink followed by a large amount of water. Rinse the piece of zinc with water and place it in a recycling container as directed by your instructor.B

B.2 Balance the equation given for the reaction. The symbol (*aq*) means aqueous (dissolved in water). *Unbalanced equation:* Zn(s) + CuSO$_4$(*aq*) $\longrightarrow$ Cu(s) + ZnSO$_4$(*aq*)

B.3 Identify the type of reaction that has occurred.

C. Metals and HCl

Materials: Three test tubes, test tube rack, small pieces of Cu(s), Zn(s), and Mg(s) metal
1 M HCl ***Caution: HCl is a corrosive acid. Handle carefully!***

C.1 Place 3 mL of 1 M HCl (match your reference volume from part B) in each of three test tubes. Describe the appearance of each metal. Carefully add a metal piece to the acid in each of the test tubes. Record any evidence of reaction such as bubbles of gas (H$_2$). Carefully pour off the acid and follow with large quantities of water to dilute. Rinse the metal pieces with water, dry, and return to your instructor.

C.2 Balance the equation given for each metal that gave a chemical reaction. If there was no reaction, cross out the products and write NR for no reaction.

Unbalanced equations: 1. Cu(s) + HCl(*aq*) $\longrightarrow$ CuCl$_2$(*aq*) + H$_2$(*g*)

2. Zn(s) + HCl(*aq*) $\longrightarrow$ ZnCl$_2$(*aq*) + H$_2$(*g*)

3. Mg(s) + HCl(*aq*) $\longrightarrow$ MgCl$_2$(*aq*) + H$_2$(*g*)

C.3 Identify the type of reaction for each chemical reaction that occurred.

D. Reactions of Ionic Compounds

Materials: Three (3) test tubes, test tube rack
Dropper bottle sets of 0.1 M solutions: CaCl$_2$, Na$_3$PO$_4$, BaCl$_2$, Na$_2$SO$_4$, FeCl$_3$, KSCN

For each of these reactions, two substances will be mixed together. Describe your observations of the reactants before you mix them and then describe the products of the reaction. Look for changes in color, the formation of a solid (solution turns cloudy), the dissolving of a solid, and/or the formation of a gas (bubbling). Balance the equations for the reactions. Dispose of the solutions properly.

D.1 Place 20 drops each of 0.1 M $CaCl_2$ (calcium chloride) and 0.1 M Na_3PO_4 (sodium phosphate) into a test tube. Describe any changes that occur. Identify the type of reaction for each chemical reaction that occurred. *Unbalanced equation:* $CaCl_2(aq) + Na_3PO_4(aq) \longrightarrow Ca_3(PO_4)_2(s) + NaCl(aq)$

D.2 Place 20 drops each of 0.1 M $BaCl_2$ (barium chloride) and 0.1 M Na_2SO_4 (sodium sulfate) into a test tube. Describe any changes that occur. Identify the type of reaction for each chemical reaction that occurred. *Unbalanced equation:* $BaCl_2(aq) + Na_2SO_4(aq) \longrightarrow BaSO_4(s) + NaCl(aq)$

D.3 Place 20 drops each of 0.1 M $FeCl_3$ (iron(III) chloride) and 0.1 M KSCN (potassium thiocyanate) into a test tube. Describe any changes that occur. Identify the type of reaction for each chemical reaction that occurred. *Unbalanced equation:*

$$FeCl_3(aq) + KSCN(aq) \longrightarrow Fe(SCN)_3(aq) + KCl(aq)$$

E. Sodium Carbonate and HCl

Materials: Test tube, test tube rack, 1 M HCl solution, $Na_2CO_3(s)$, and matches or wood splints

E.1 Place about 3 mL of 1 M HCl in a test tube. Add a small amount of solid Na_2CO_3 (about the size of a pea) to the test tube. Record your observations. ***Caution: HCl is corrosive. Clean up any spills immediately. If spilled on the skin, flood the area with water for at least 10 minutes.***

E.2 Identify the type of reaction for each chemical reaction that occurred.
Unbalanced equation: $Na_2CO_3(s) + HCl(aq) \longrightarrow CO_2(g) + H_2O(l) + NaCl(aq)$

E.3 Light a match or wood splint and insert the flame inside the neck of the test tube. What happens to the flame? Record your observations.

Report Sheet

Date _____   Name _____

Section _____   Team _____

Instructor _____   _____

Pre-Lab Study Questions

1. Why is the freezing of water called a physical change?

2. Why are burning candles and rusting nails examples of chemical change?

3. What is included in a chemical equation?

4. How does a combination reaction differ from a decomposition reaction?

A. Magnesium and Oxygen

A.1 Initial appearance of Mg   _____

_____

   Observations of the reaction   _____

_____

   Appearance of the product   _____

_____

A.2 Balance: _____$Mg(s)$ + _____ $O_2(g)$ _____ $MgO(s)$

A.3 Type of reaction: _____

_____

Report Sheet

B. Zinc and Copper(II) Sulfate

B.1   Initially   Zn _____

CuSO$_4$ _____

15 min   Zn _____

CuSO$_4$ _____

30 min   Zn _____

CuSO$_4$ _____

B.2   Balance: ____ Zn(s)   + _____ CuSO$_4$(aq) $\longrightarrow$ ____ Cu(s)   + ____ ZnSO$_4$(aq)

B.3   Type of reaction: _____

_____

C. Metals and HCl

C.1   Observations

Cu   Initial: _____

Reaction: _____

Zn   Initial: _____

Reaction: _____

Mg   Initial: _____

Reaction: _____

C.2   Balance: ____ Cu(s) + ____ HCl(aq) $\longrightarrow$ ____ CuCl$_2$(aq) + ____ H$_2$(g)

____ Zn(s) + ____ HCl(aq) $\longrightarrow$ ____ ZnCl$_2$(aq) + ____ H$_2$(g)

____ Mg(s) + ____ HCl(aq) $\longrightarrow$ ____ MgCl$_2$(aq) + ____ H$_2$(g)

C.3   Type of reaction: Cu _____

Zn _____

Mg _____

Report Sheet

D. Reactions of Ionic Compounds

D.1 **CaCl₂ and Na₃PO₄**

Observations:_____

_____

Type of reaction: _____

Balance: ____CaCl$_2$(*aq*) + ____ Na$_3$PO$_4$(*aq*) $\longrightarrow$ ____ Ca$_3$(PO$_4$)$_2$(*s*) + ____ NaCl(*aq*)

D.2 **BaCl₂ and Na₂SO₄**

Observations:_____

_____

Type of reaction: _____

Balance: ____ BaCl$_2$(*aq*) + ____ Na$_2$SO$_4$(*aq*) $\longrightarrow$ ____ BaSO$_4$(*s*) + ____ NaCl(*aq*)

D.3 **FeCl₃ and KSCN**

Observations:_____

_____

Type of reaction: _____

Balance: ____ FeCl$_3$(*aq*) + ____ KSCN(*aq*) $\longrightarrow$ ____ Fe(SCN)$_3$(*aq*) + ____ KCl(*aq*)

E. Sodium Carbonate and HCl

E.1 Observations:_____

_____

E.2 Type of reaction: _____

Balance: ____ Na$_2$CO$_3$(*s*) + ____ HCl(*aq*) $\longrightarrow$ ____ CO$_2$(*g*) + ____ H$_2$O(*l*) + ____ NaCl(*aq*)

E.3 Why did the flame of the burning match or splint go out?

Report Sheet

Questions and Problems

Q.1 What evidence of a chemical reaction might you see in the following cases?

    a. Dropping an Alka-Seltzer™ tablet into a glass of water

        _____

    b. Bleaching a stain

        _____

    c. Burning a match

        _____

    d. Rusting of an iron nail

        _____

Q.2 Balance the following equations:

    a. ____ $Mg(s)$ + ____ $HCl(aq)$ $\longrightarrow$ ____ $H_2(g)$ + ____ $MgCl_2(aq)$

    b. ____ $Al(s)$ + ____ $O_2(g)$ $\longrightarrow$ ____ $Al_2O_3(s)$

    c. ____ $Fe_2O_3(s)$ + ____ $H_2O(l)$ $\longrightarrow$ ____ $Fe(OH)_3(s)$

    d. ____ $Ca(OH)_2(aq)$ + ____ $HNO_3(aq)$ $\longrightarrow$ ____ $Ca(NO_3)_2(aq)$ + ____ $H_2O(l)$

Q.3 Write an equation for the following reactions. Remember that gases of elements such as oxygen are diatomic (O_2). Write the *correct formulas* of the reactants and products. Then correctly balance each equation.

    a. Potassium and oxygen gas react to form potassium oxide.

    b. Sodium and water react to form sodium hydroxide and hydrogen gas.

    c. Iron and oxygen gas react to form iron(III) oxide.

Report Sheet

Q.4 Classify each reaction as combination (C), decomposition (DC), single replacement (SR), or double replacement (DR).

  a. $Ni + F_2 \quad\quad NiF_2$ _____

  b. $Fe_2O_3 + 3C \quad\quad 2Fe + 3CO$ _____

  c. $CaCO_3 \quad\quad CaO + CO_2$ _____

  d. $H_2SO_4 + 2KOH \quad\quad K_2SO_4 + 2H_2O$ _____

Q.5 Predict what product(s) would form from the reaction of the following reactants:

  a. $Zn + CuBr_2 \longrightarrow$ _____ + _____

  b. $H_2 + Cl_2 \longrightarrow$ _____

  c. $MgCO_3 \longrightarrow$ _____ + _____

  d. $KCl + AgNO_3 \longrightarrow$ _____ + _____

Energy and Matter

Goals

- Prepare a heating curve for water.
- Use the specific heat of water to calculate heat lost or gained.
- Calculate the heat of fusion for water.
- Use the nutrition data on food products to determine the kilocalories in one serving.
- Identify a reaction as exothermic or endothermic.

Discussion

A. A Heating Curve for Water

The temperature of a substance indicates the kinetic energy (energy of motion) of its molecules. When water molecules gain heat energy, they move faster and the temperature rises. Eventually the water molecules gain sufficient energy to separate from the other liquid molecules. The liquid changes to a gas in a change of state called *boiling*. The change of state from liquid to gas is indicated when the water temperature becomes constant. It is more obvious when a graph is drawn of the temperature change of the substance that is heated. When a liquid boils, a horizontal line (*plateau*) appears on the graph, as shown in Figure 1. This constant temperature is called its *boiling point*.

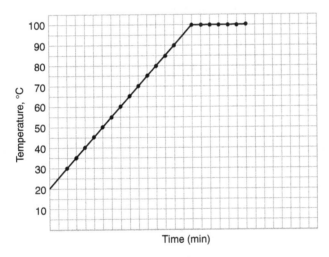

Figure 1   Example of a graph of a heating curve

Measuring Heat

When two substances are in contact, the heat from one can be transferred to the other. When you put ice in a warm drink, the heat from the drink is transferred to the ice. The ice melts and the drink cools. The drink lost heat and the ice gained heat. By measuring the change in temperature of the drink, we can determine the amount of heat transferred to the ice.

Heat lost (by warm drink)   =   heat gained (by ice)

From *Essential Laboratory Manual for Chemistry: An Introduction to General, Organic, and Biological Chemistry*, Ninth Edition, Karen C. Timberlake. Copyright © 2007 by Pearson Education, Inc. Published by Benjamin Cummings. All rights reserved.

The amount of heat transferred depends on the specific heat of the substance. Specific heat refers to the amount of heat required to raise the temperature of 1 g of a substance by 1°C.

$$\text{Specific heat of water} \ = \ \frac{1.00 \text{ calorie}}{1 \text{ g} \ \times \ 1°C}$$

Water has a specific heat of 1.00 calorie per g °C. The heat energy (calories) is calculated using the mass (g) of water, the change in temperature (ΔT), and the specific heat of water, according to the following:

Heat (cal) = mass of water (g) × temperature change (ΔT) × specific heat (1.00 cal/g °C)

B. Energy in Changes of State

Heat of Fusion

Changing state from solid to liquid (melting) requires energy. Ice melts at 0°C, a constant temperature. At that melting point, the amount of heat required to melt 1 g of ice is called the *heat of fusion*. For water, the energy needed to melt 1 g of ice (0°C) is 80. calories. That is also the amount of heat released when liquid water freezes to solid ice at 0°C.

Melting (0°C): $H_2O(s)$ + heat$_{fusion}$ (80. cal/g) $\longrightarrow$ $H_2O(l)$

Freezing (0°C): $H_2O(l)$ $\longrightarrow$ $H_2O(s)$ + heat$_{fusion}$ (80. cal/g)

In this experiment, ice will be added to a sample of water. From the temperature change, the amount of heat lost by the water sample can be calculated. This is also the amount of heat needed to melt the ice.

Heat (cal) lost by water = heat (cal) gained to melt ice

= g water × ΔT × 1.00 cal/g °C

By measuring the amount of ice that melted, the heat of fusion can be calculated as follows:

$$\text{Heat of fusion (cal/g)} \ = \ \frac{\text{heat (cal) gained to melt ice}}{\text{grams of ice}}$$

Heat of Vaporization

A similar situation occurs for a substance that changes from a liquid to a gas (vapor). Water boils at 100°C, its boiling point. At that temperature, the energy required to convert liquid to gas is called the *heat of vaporization*. For water, the energy required to vaporize 1 g of water at 100°C is 540 calories. This is also the amount of heat released when 1 gram of steam condenses to liquid at 100°C.

Boiling (100°C): $H_2O(l)$ + heat$_{vaporization}$ (540 cal/g) $\longrightarrow$ $H_2O(g)$

Condensation (100°C): $H_2O(g)$ $\longrightarrow$ $H_2O(l)$ + heat$_{vaporization}$ (540 cal/g)

C. Food Calories

Our diets contain foods that provide us with energy. We need energy to make our muscles work, to breathe, to synthesize molecules in the body such as protein and fats, and to repair tissues. A typical diet required by a 25-year-old woman is about 2000–2500 kcal. By contrast, a bicycle rider or a ballerina with a higher energy requirement may need a diet that provides 4000 kcal. The nutritional energy of food is determined in Calories (Cal), which are the same as 1000 cal or 1 kilocalorie.

Calorimetric experiments have established the caloric values for the three food types: carbohydrates, 4 kcal/g; fats, 9 kcal/g; and proteins, 4 kcal/g. By measuring the amount of each food type in a serving, the kilocalories can be calculated. For example, a candy that is composed of 12 g of carbohydrate will provide 48 kcal. Usually the values are rounded to the nearest tens place.

$$12 \text{ g carbohydrate} \times \frac{4 \text{ Kcal}}{1 \text{ g carbohydrate}} = 48 \text{ kcal or } 50 \text{ kcal}$$

D. Exothermic and Endothermic Reactions

In an *exothermic* reaction, heat is released, which causes the temperature of the surroundings to increase. An *endothermic* reaction absorbs heat, which causes a drop in the temperature of the surroundings. Heat can be written as a product for an exothermic reaction and as a reactant for an endothermic reaction. Energy is required to break apart bonds and is released when bonds form. If energy is released by forming bonds, the reaction is exothermic. If energy is required to break apart bonds, the reaction is endothermic. In our cells, the bonds in carbohydrates are broken down to give us energy. Reactions that build molecules and repair cells are endothermic because they require energy.

Exothermic reactions: $C + O_2 \longrightarrow CO_2 + \text{heat}$

$C_6H_{12}O_6 + 6O_2 \longrightarrow 6CO_2 + 6H_2O + \text{energy}$
Glucose

Endothermic reactions: $\text{Heat} + PCl_5 \longrightarrow PCl_3 + Cl_2$

$\text{Energy} + \text{amino acids} \longrightarrow \text{protein}$

Lab Information

Time: 2 hr
Comments: Tear out the report sheets and place them beside the matching procedures.
                 Be careful with boiling water.
                 Use mitts or beaker tongs to move hot beakers, or let them cool.
Related Topics: Changes of state, heating and cooling curves, measuring heat energy, calorie

Experimental Procedures

A.   A Heating Curve for Water

Materials: Beaker (250- or 400-mL), Bunsen burner (or hot plate), ring stand, graduated cylinder, iron ring, wire gauze, clamp, thermometer, timer

Using a graduated cylinder, pour 100 mL of cool water into a 250-mL beaker. As shown in Figure 2, place the beaker on a hot plate or on a wire screen placed on an iron ring above a Bunsen burner. The height of the iron ring should be about 3–5 cm above the burner. Tie a string to the loop in the top of the thermometer or place the thermometer securely in a clamp. Adjust the thermometer so that the bulb is in the center portion of the liquid. (Do not let the thermometer rest on the side or bottom of the beaker.)

A.1 Measure and record the initial temperature of the water. Light the burner (or use a hot plate). Using a timer or a watch with a second hand, record the temperature of the water at 1-minute intervals. Eventually the water will come to a *full boil*. (The early appearance of small bubbles of escaping gas does not indicate boiling.) When the water is boiling, the temperature has become constant. Record the boiling temperature for another 4–5 minutes.

A.2 Prepare a heating curve for water by graphing the temperature versus the time. Review graphing data found in the preface. Label the parts of the graph that represent the liquid state and boiling.

A.3 The plateau (flat part of graph) indicates the *boiling point* of the water. Record its value.

A.4 Calculate the temperature change needed for the cool water to reach the boiling point (plateau).

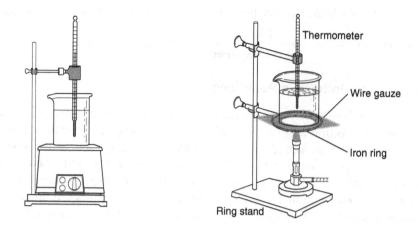

Figure 2   Setup for heating water with (left) a hot plate or (right) a Bunsen burner

A.5   Using the measured volume of water and its density (1.00 g/mL), calculate the mass of the water.

A.6   Calculate the heat in calories used to heat the water to the boiling point.

Calories   =   mass   × ΔT ×   1.00 cal/g °C

B.   Energy in Changes of State

Materials: Calorimeter (Styrofoam® cup and cardboard cover), thermometer, 50- or 100-mL graduated cylinder, 100-mL beaker, ice

B.1   Weigh an empty Styrofoam cup.

B.2   Add 100 mL of water to the cup and reweigh.

B.3   Record the initial temperature of the water in the calorimeter. See Figure 3. Add 2 or 3 ice cubes (or crushed ice that fills a 100-mL beaker) to the water in the cup. Stir strongly. Check the temperature of the ice water. Add ice until the temperature drops to 2–3°C. If some ice is not melted, remove it immediately. Record the final temperature of the water.

B.4   Weigh the Styrofoam (calorimetry) cup with the initial sample of water and the melted ice. The increase in mass indicates the amount of ice that melted.

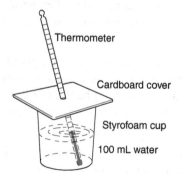

Figure 3   Calorimetry setup with water, a thermometer, Styrofoam cup, and a cardboard cover

Calculations

B.5 Calculate the mass of water added to the Styrofoam cup.

B.6 Calculate the temperature change (ΔT) for the water.

B.7 Calculate the calories lost by the water.

Heat (cal) lost by water $=$ mass of water $\times \Delta T \times$ specific heat (1.00 cal/g $°C$)

This is the same number of calories that melted the ice.

B.8 Calculate the grams of ice that melted by subtracting the initial mass of the cup and water from the final mass of the cup and water after the ice melted.

B.9 Calculate your experimental value for the heat of fusion for ice.

$$\text{Heat of fusion (cal / g)} = \frac{\text{heat (cal) gained to melt ice}}{\text{grams of ice}}$$

C. Food Calories

Materials: Food products with nutrition data on labels

C.1 Obtain a food product that has a *Nutrition Facts* label. Indicate the serving size.

C.2 List the grams of fat, carbohydrate, and protein in one serving of the food.

C.3 From the mass of each food type, calculate the Calories (kcal) of each food type in one serving. Use their accepted caloric values.

C.4 Determine the total Calories (kcal) in one serving.

C.5 Compare your total to the Calories listed on the upper portion of the label. Usually these totals are rounded to the nearest tens place.

D. Exothermic and Endothermic Reactions

Materials: Two test tubes, water, scoop or spatula, $NH_4NO_3(s)$, $CaCl_2(s)$ anhydrous, thermometer

D.1 Place 5 mL of water in each of two test tubes. Record the temperature of the water. Add one scoop of $NH_4NO_3(s)$ crystals to the water in the first test tube. Add one scoop of anhydrous $CaCl_2(s)$ to the water in the second test tube. *Anhydrous* means "without water." Stir each and record the temperature again.

$$NH_4NO_3(s) \xrightarrow{\text{H}_2\text{O}} NH_4^+(aq) + NO_3^-(aq)$$

$$CaCl_2(s) \xrightarrow{\text{H}_2\text{O}} Ca^{2+}(aq) + 2\,Cl^-(aq)$$

D.2 Describe each reaction as endothermic or exothermic.

D.3 To each equation, add the term *heat* on the side of the reactants (if endothermic) and on the side of the products (if exothermic).

Report Sheet

Date _____   Name _____

Section _____   Team _____

Instructor _____   _____

Pre-Lab Study Questions

1. Why is energy required for the melting or boiling process?

2. How does an exothermic reaction differ from an endothermic reaction?

A. A Heating Curve for Water

Volume of water: _____ mL

A.1

Time (min)	Temperature (°C)	Time (min)	Temperature (°C)
0	_____	_____	_____
1	_____	_____	_____
2	_____	_____	_____
_____	_____	_____	_____
_____	_____	_____	_____
_____	_____	_____	_____
_____	_____	_____	_____
_____	_____	_____	_____
_____	_____	_____	_____
_____	_____	_____	_____

A.2 Graphing the Heating Curve

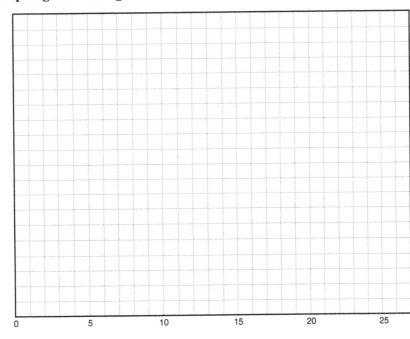

Temperature (°C)

Time (min)

79

Report Sheet

A.3 Boiling point of water   _____ °C

A.4 Temperature change (ΔT)   _____ °C

A.5 Volume of water   _____ mL

     Mass of water   _____ g

A.6 Number of calories needed to heat water   _____ cal
     (*Show calculations.*)

Questions and Problems

Q.1 On the heating curve, how long did it take for the temperature to rise to 60°C?

B. Energy in Changes of State

B.1 Empty calorimeter cup   _____ g

B.2 Calorimeter + water   _____ g

B.3 *Final* water temperature   _____ °C

     Initial water temperature   _____ °C

B.4 Calorimeter + water + melted ice   _____ g

Calculations

B.5 Mass of water   _____ g

B.6 Temperature change   _____ °C

B.7 Calories lost by water   _____ cal
     (*Show calculations.*)

     Calories used to melt ice   _____ cal

B.8 Mass of ice that melted   _____ g
     (*Show calculations.*)

B.9 Heat of fusion (calories to melt 1 g of ice)   _____ cal/g
     (*Show calculations.*)

Report Sheet

Questions and Problems

Q.2 When water is heated, the temperature eventually reaches a constant value and forms a plateau on the graph. What does the plateau indicate?

Q.3 175 g of water was heated from 15° to 88°C. How many kilocalories were absorbed by the water?

Q.4 How many calories are required at 0°C to melt an ice cube with a mass of 25 g?

Q.5 a. Calculate the amount of heat (kcal) released when 50.0 g of water at 100°C hits the skin and cools to a body temperature of 37°C.

b. Calculate the amount of heat (kcal) released when 50.0 g of steam at 100°C hits the skin, condenses, and cools to a body temperature of 37°C.

c. Use your answer in 5a and 5b to explain why steam burns are so severe.

Report Sheet

C. Food Calories

C.1 Name of food product _____ Serving size_____

C.2 Mass of food types in one serving

Carbohydrate _____ g   Fat_____ g   Protein _____ g

C.3 Calculations for kcal per serving
(*Show calculations.*)
Carbohydrate   _____ kcal (Cal)

Fat   _____ kcal (Cal)

Protein   _____ kcal (Cal)

C.4 Total Calories (kcal) per serving   _____ kcal (Cal)

C.5 Calories (for one serving) listed on the label   _____ Cal

Questions and Problems

Q.6 What percent (%) of the total Calories in your food product is from fat?

What percent (%) of the total Calories in your food product is from carbohydrate?

What percent (%) of the total Calories in your food product is from protein?

Q.7 How does your calculated number of Calories compare to the Calories listed on the label of the food product?

Report Sheet

D. Exothermic and Endothermic Reactions

D.1

	NH_4NO_3 Tube	$CaCl_2$ Tube
Initial temperature	_____	_____
Final temperature	_____	_____
Temperature change	_____	_____

D.2 Endothermic or exothermic _____   _____

D.3 Equations (add *heat*)

$$NH_4NO_3(s) \xrightarrow{\;H_2O\;} NH_4^+(aq) + NO_3^-(aq)$$

$$CaCl_2(s) \xrightarrow{\;H_2O\;} Ca^{2+}(aq) + 2\,Cl^-(aq)$$

Questions and Problems

Q.8 As a lab technician for a pharmaceutical company, you are responsible for preparing hot packs and cold packs. A hot pack involves the release of heat when a salt and water are mixed. A cold pack becomes colder because mixing a salt and water absorbs heat.

From the experiment, which compound could you use to make a hot pack?

From the experiment, which compound could you use to make a cold pack?

Q.9 When you burn a log in the fireplace or burn gasoline in a car, is the reaction (combustion) an endothermic or exothermic reaction? Why?

Solutions

Goals

- Observe the solubility of a solute in polar and nonpolar solvents.
- Determine the effect of particle size, stirring, and temperature on the rate of solution formation.
- Identify an unsaturated and a saturated solution.
- Observe the effect of temperature on solubility.
- Measure the solubility of KNO_3 at various temperatures, and graph a solubility curve.
- Calculate the mass/mass percent and mass/volume percent concentrations for a NaCl solution.
- Calculate the molar concentration of the NaCl solution.

Discussion

A. Polarity of Solutes and Solvents

A solution is a mixture of the particles of two or more substances. The substance that is present in the greater amount is called the *solvent*. The substance that is present in the smaller amount is the *solute*. In many solutions, including body fluids and the oceans, water is the solvent. Water is considered the *universal solvent*. However, the solutes and solvents that make up solutions may be solids, liquids, or gases. Carbonated beverages are solutions of CO_2 gas in water.

A solution forms when the attractive forces between the solute and the solvent are similar. A polar (or ionic) solute such as NaCl is soluble in water, a polar solvent. As the NaCl dissolves, its ions separate into Na^+ and Cl^-. The positive Na^+ ions are attracted to the partially negative oxygen atoms of water. At the same time, the negative Cl^- ions are pulled into the solvent by their attraction to the partially positive hydrogen atoms of water. The ions stay in solution because they are hydrated, which means that a group of water molecules is attracted to each ion.

Water, which is polar, dissolves polar solutes such as glucose and salt, NaCl. A nonpolar solvent such as acetone is needed to dissolve a nonpolar solute such as nail polish. This requirement of similar electrical attraction between solute and solvent is sometimes stated as "like dissolves like."

B. Solubility of KNO₃

When a solution holds the maximum amount of solute at a certain temperature, it is *saturated*. When more solute is added, the excess appears as a solid in the container. The maximum amount of solute that dissolves is called the *solubility* of that solute in that solvent. Solubility is usually stated as the number of grams of solute that dissolve in 100 mL (or 100 g) of water. The solubility depends upon several factors, including the nature of the solute and solvent, the temperature, and the pressure (for a gas). Most solids are more soluble in water at higher temperatures. Generally, the dissolving of a solid solute is endothermic, which means that solubility increases with an increase in temperature.

From *Essential Laboratory Manual for Chemistry: An Introduction to General, Organic, and Biological Chemistry*, Ninth Edition, Karen C. Timberlake. Copyright © 2007 by Pearson Education, Inc. Published by Benjamin Cummings. All rights reserved.

C.   Concentration of a Sodium Chloride Solution

The concentration of a solution is calculated from the amount of solute present in a certain amount of solution. The concentration may be expressed using different units for amount of solute and solution. A *mass/mass percent* concentration expresses the grams of solute in the grams of solution. The *mass/volume percent* concentration of a solution states the grams of solute present in the milliliters of the solution.

$$\text{mass/mass percent (m/m)} = \frac{\text{grams of solute}}{\text{grams of solution}} \times 100$$

$$\text{mass/volume percent (m/v)} = \frac{\text{grams of solute}}{\text{milliliters of solution}} \times 100$$

A *molar* (M) concentration gives the moles of solute in a liter of solution.

$$\text{molarity (M)} = \frac{\text{moles of solute}}{\text{1 liter of solution}}$$

In this experiment, you will measure a 10.0-mL volume of a sodium chloride solution. The mass of the solution will be determined by weighing the solution in a preweighed evaporating dish. After the sample is evaporated to dryness, it is weighed again. From this data, the mass of the salt (solute) is obtained.

Using the mass of the solute and the mass of the solution, the mass/mass (m/m) percent can be calculated. From the mass of the solute and the volume (mL) of the solution, the mass/volume (m/v) percent can be calculated. To calculate the molarity of the solution, convert the mass of the solute to moles, and the volume to liters (L).

The saturation of a solution is observed when crystals of the salt appear. This is commonly seen in iced drinks after sugar has been added. As soon as the drink is saturated with sugar, the sugar that exceeds the solubility forms a layer in the bottom of the glass. By cooling a solution and watching for the appearance of crystals of solute in the liquid solution, you can determine the temperature at which solubility is reached.

Lab Information

Time: 2 hr

Comments: Some solvents in part A of the experiments are flammable. Do not light any burners. Tear out the report sheets and place them beside the matching procedures.

Related Topics: Solute, solvent, formation of solutions, polar and nonpolar solutes, saturated solution, solubility, concentrations of solutions

Experimental Procedures

Laboratory goggles must be worn!

A. Polarity of Solutes and Solvents

This may be a demonstration by your instructor.

Materials: Test tubes (8), test tube rack, spatulas, stirring rods, $KMnO_4(s)$, $I_2(s)$, sucrose(s), vegetable oil, cyclohexane

A.1 **Solubility of solutes in a polar solvent** Set up four test tubes in a test tube rack. To each test tube, add a few crystals (or a few drops) of a solute: $KMnO_4$, I_2, sucrose, or vegetable oil. To each, add 3 mL of water and stir the mixture with a glass stirring rod. Describe each solute as soluble or not soluble in the water, a polar solvent. Save for comparison to the test tubes in A.2.

A.2 **Solubility of solutes in a nonpolar solvent** To a different set of four test tubes, add a few crystals (or a few drops) of a solute: $KMnO_4$, I_2, sucrose, or vegetable oil. Place 3 mL of cyclohexane, a nonpolar solvent, in each. ***Caution: Cyclohexane is <u>flammable</u>—do not proceed if any laboratory burners are in use.***

Indicate whether each solute is soluble or not soluble in cyclohexane, a nonpolar solvent. Compare the solubility of the solutes in cyclohexane (A.2) with their solubility in water (A.1). Discard the solutions for A.1 and A.2 in the waste containers provided in the lab, *NOT* in the sink. *Iodine (I_2) can burn the skin. Handle cautiously!*

A.3 Determine the polarity of each solute from its solubility in each type of solvent. If a solute dissolves in a polar solvent like water, it is a polar solute. If a solute dissolves in a nonpolar solvent like cyclohexane, the solute is nonpolar.

B. Solubility of KNO_3

Materials: Weighing paper or small container, spatula, stirring rod, large test tube, 400-mL beaker, buret clamp, hot plate or Bunsen burner, thermometer, 10-mL graduated cylinder, $KNO_3(s)$

To reduce the amount of KNO_3 used, each group of students will be assigned an amount of KNO_3 to weigh out. The results will be shared with the class.

B.1 Obtain a piece of weighing paper or a small container and weigh it carefully. (Or you may tare the container.)

B.2 Each group of students will be assigned an amount of KNO_3 from 2 to 7 grams. Weigh out an amount of KNO_3 that is close to your assigned amount. For example, if you are assigned an amount of 3 grams, measure out a mass such as 3.10 g or 3.25 g or 2.85 g. It is not necessary to add or remove KNO_3 to obtain exactly 3.00 g. Weigh carefully. Calculate the mass of KNO_3.

> ***Taring a container on an electronic balance:*** The mass of a container on an electronic balance can be set to 0 by pressing the tare bar. As a substance is added to the container, the mass shown on the readout is for the substance only. (When a container is *tared*, it is not necessary to subtract the mass of the beaker.)

B.3 *The temperature at which the KNO₃ is soluble is determined by heating and cooling the KNO₃* solution. Place 5.0 mL of water in a large test tube. Add your weighed amount of KNO₃. Clamp the test tube to a ring stand and place the test tube in a beaker of water. Use a hot plate or Bunsen burner to heat the water. See Figure 1. Stir the mixture and continue heating until all the KNO₃ dissolves.

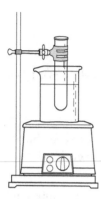

Figure 1   Heating the KNO₃ solution in a water bath

As soon as all the KNO₃ dissolves, turn off the burner. Loosen the clamp and remove the test tube from the hot water. As the test tube and contents cool, stir gently with a thermometer. Look closely for the first appearance of crystals. As soon as you see some solid crystals, read the temperature of the solution. Record. This is the temperature at which the solution becomes saturated. The amount of KNO₃ in that solution is the solubility of KNO₃ at that temperature.

Place the test tube back into the hot water bath and begin heating again. Repeat the warming and cooling of the solution until you have obtained three or more temperature readings that agree. Set the test tube aside. In 15–20 minutes, observe the appearance of the crystals in the test tube.

To discard, add water and heat until the KNO₃ dissolves. Pour the solution in proper waste containers provided in the laboratory, *NOT* in the sink. (Solid KNO₃ can be recovered from the solution by evaporation to dryness.)

Calculations

B.4 Solubility is expressed as the number of grams of solute in 100 mL of water. Because you used a sample of 5.0 mL of water, the mass of the solute you measured out and the 5.0 mL of water are both multiplied by 20.

$$\frac{\text{g KNO}_3}{5.0 \text{ mL water}} \times \frac{20}{20} = \frac{\text{g KNO}_3}{100 \text{ mL water}} = \text{Solubility (g KNO}_3 \text{ per 100 mL water)}$$

Collect the solubility results of other KNO₃ solutions and their solubility temperatures from the other groups of students in the lab.

B.5 Prepare a graph of the solubility curve for KNO₃. Plot the solubility (g KNO₃/100 mL water) on the vertical axis and the temperature (0–100°C) on the horizontal axis.

C. Concentration of a Sodium Chloride Solution

Materials: Hot plate (or Bunsen burner, iron ring, and wire screen), evaporating dish, NaCl solution, 400-mL beaker (to fit evaporating dish), 10-mL graduated cylinder (or 10-mL pipet)

C.1 Weigh a dry evaporating dish. Record the mass. *Do not round off.*

C.2 Using a 10.0-mL graduated cylinder, or a 10.0-mL pipet, measure out a 10.0-mL sample of the NaCl solution. See Figure 2. Record this volume.

Using a pipet: Place the pipet bulb on the upper end of the pipet. Squeeze the bulb about halfway. Place the tapered end of the pipet in the liquid. As the bulb inflates, liquid will move into the pipet. The level of liquid should rise above the volume mark, but not into the bulb. Remove the bulb and quickly cover the pipet with your *index* finger. Adjust the pressure of your finger to slowly drain the liquid until the level is at the volume mark. You may need to practice. With your finger still on the pipet, lift the pipet out of the liquid and move it to the evaporating dish. Lift your finger off the pipet to let the liquid flow out. Some liquid should remain in the tip.

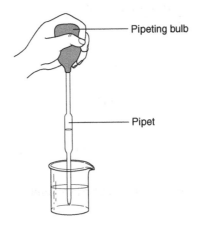

— Pipeting bulb

— Pipet

Figure 2 Using a pipet

C.3 Weigh the evaporating dish and the NaCl solution. Record.

C.4 Fill a 400-mL beaker about half full of water. Set on a hot plate, or heat with a Bunsen burner using an iron ring with a wire screen. Place the evaporating dish on top of the beaker. Heat the water in the beaker to boiling. See Figure 3. You may need to add more water to the bath as you proceed.

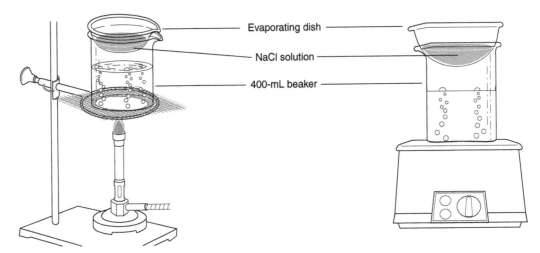

— Evaporating dish

— NaCl solution

— 400-mL beaker

Figure 3 Using a Bunsen burner or hot plate to evaporate a salt solution

When the NaCl appears to be dry or begins to pop, turn off the burner. After the evaporating dish has cooled, dry the bottom and place it directly on the hot plate or in the iron ring. Heat gently with a low flame to dry the salt completely. Allow the evaporating dish and dried NaCl sample to cool. Weigh the evaporating dish and the dry NaCl. Record. *Do not round off.*

Calculations

C.5 Calculate the mass of the solution.

C.6 Calculate the mass of the NaCl after drying. Subtract the mass of the evaporating dish from the total mass of the evaporating dish and the dried salt.

C.7 Calculate the mass/mass percent concentration.

$$\text{Mass/mass percent} = \frac{\text{Mass of dry NaCl}}{\text{mass (g) of solution}} \times 100$$

C.8 Calculate the mass/volume percent concentration.

$$\text{Mass/volume percent} = \frac{\text{Mass of dry NaCl}}{\text{volume (mL) of solution}} \times 100$$

C.9 Calculate the moles of NaCl. The molar mass of NaCl is 58.5 g/mole.

$$\text{g of dried NaCl} \times \frac{1 \text{ mole NaCl}}{58.5 \text{ g NaCl}} = \text{moles NaCl}$$

C.10 Convert the volume in mL of the solution to the corresponding volume in liters.

$$\text{mL of NaCl solution} \times \frac{1 \text{ L}}{1000 \text{ mL}} = \text{L of NaCl solution}$$

C.11 Calculate the molarity of the NaCl solution.

$$\text{Molarity (M)} = \frac{\text{moles NaCl}}{\text{L of solution}}$$

Report Sheet

Date _____   Name _____

Section _____   Team _____

Instructor _____

Pre-Lab Study Questions

1. Why does an oil-and-vinegar salad dressing have two separate layers?

2. What is meant by the mass/mass percent concentration of a solution?

3. What is molarity?

A. Polarity of Solutes and Solvents

Solute	Soluble/Not Soluble in		Identify the Solute as Polar or Nonpolar (A.3)
	Water (A.1)	Cyclohexane (A.2)	
$KMnO_4$			
I_2			
Sucrose			
Vegetable oil			

NaCl is soluble in water, but I_2 is not. Explain.

State the general solubility rule concerning the polarities of a solute and solvent.

Report Sheet

B. Solubility of KNO₃

B.1 Mass of Container	B.2 Mass of Container + KNO₃	Mass of KNO₃	B.3 Temperature (Crystals Appear)	B.4 Solubility (g KNO₃/100 mL H₂O)

B.5 Graphing the solubility of KNO₃ vs. temperature (°C)

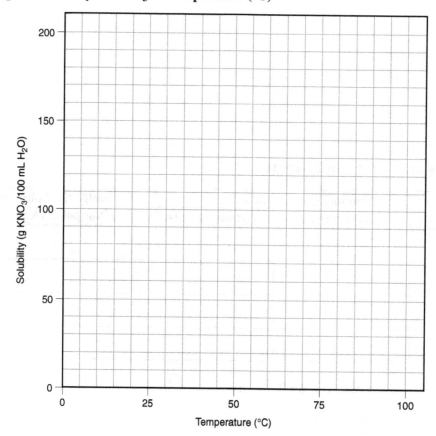

According to your graph, what is the effect of increasing temperature on the solubility of KNO₃?

On your solubility curve, what is the change in solubility of KNO₃ from 30°C to 60°C?

At what temperature is the solubility of KNO₃ 50 g/100 mL H₂O?

Report Sheet

Questions and Problems

Q.1 The solubility of sucrose (common table sugar) at 70°C is 320 g/100 g H_2O.
a. How much sucrose can dissolve in 200 g of water at 70°C?

b. Will 400 g of sucrose dissolve in a teapot that contains 200 g of water at 70°C? Explain.

C. Concentration of a Sodium Chloride Solution

C.1 Mass of evaporating dish   _____ g

C.2 Volume of NaCl solution   _____ mL

C.3 Mass of dish and NaCl solution   _____ g

C.4 Mass of dish and dry NaCl   _____ g

Calculations

C.5 Mass of NaCl solution   _____ g

C.6 Mass of the dry NaCl salt   _____ g

C.7 Mass/mass percent   _____% (m/m)
     (*Show calculations.*)

C.8 Mass/volume percent   _____% (m/v)
     (*Show calculations.*)

C.9 Moles of NaCl   _____ moles
     (*Show calculations.*)

C.10 Volume of sample in liters   _____ L

C.11 Molarity of NaCl solution   _____ M
     (*Show calculations.*)

Report Sheet

Questions and Problems

Q.2 A 15.0-mL sample of NaCl solution has a mass of 15.78 g. After the NaCl solution is evaporated to dryness, the dry salt residue has a mass of 3.26 g. Calculate the following concentrations for the NaCl solution.

a. % (m/m)

b. % (m/v)

c. molarity (M)

Q.3 How many grams of KI are in 25.0 mL of a 3.0 % (m/v) KI solution?

Q.4 How many milliliters of a 2.5 M $MgCl_2$ solution contain 17.5 g $MgCl_2$?

Acids and Bases

Goals

- Prepare a naturally occurring dye to use as a pH indicator.
- Measure the pH of several substances using cabbage indicator and a pH meter.
- Calculate pH from the [H^+] or the [OH^-] of a solution.
- Calculate the molar concentration and percentage of acetic acid in vinegar.

Discussion

An *acid* is a substance that dissolves in water and donates a hydrogen ion, or proton (H^+), to water. In the laboratory we have been using acids such as hydrochloric acid (HCl) and nitric acid (HNO_3).

$$HCl \ + \ H_2O \ \longrightarrow \ H_3O^+ \ + \ Cl^-$$
hydronium ion

You use acids and bases every day. There are acids in oranges, lemons, vinegar, and bleach. In this experiment we will use acetic acid ($HC_2H_3O_2$); the acid in vinegar that gives it a sour taste.

A *base* is a substance that accepts a proton. Some household bases include ammonia, detergents, and oven-cleaning products. Some typical bases used in the laboratory are sodium hydroxide (NaOH) and potassium hydroxide (KOH). Most of the common bases dissolve in water and produce hydroxide ions, OH^-.

$$NaOH \ \longrightarrow \ Na^+ \ + \ OH^-$$

An important weak base found in the laboratory and in some household cleaners is ammonia. In water, it reacts to form ammonium and hydroxide ions:

$$NH_3 \ + \ H_2O \ \longrightarrow \ NH_4^+ \ + \ OH^-$$

In a *neutralization* reaction, the protons (H^+) from the acid combine with hydroxide ions (OH^-) from the base to produce water (H_2O). The remaining substance is a salt, which is composed of ions from the acid and base. For example, the neutralization of HCl by NaOH is written as

$$HCl \ + \ NaOH \ \longrightarrow \ NaCl \ + \ H_2O$$

If we write the ionic substances in the equation as ions, we see that the H^+ and the OH^- form water.

$$H^+ \ + \ Cl^- \ + \ Na^+ \ + \ OH^- \ \longrightarrow \ Na^+ \ + \ Cl^- \ + \ H_2O$$

$$H^+ \qquad\qquad\quad + \ OH^- \ \longrightarrow \ H_2O$$

In a complete neutralization, the amount of H^+ will be equal to the amount of OH^-.

From *Essential Laboratory Manual for Chemistry: An Introduction to General, Organic, and Biological Chemistry*, Ninth Edition, Karen C. Timberlake. Copyright © 2007 by Pearson Education, Inc. Published by Benjamin Cummings. All rights reserved.

Acids and Bases

A. pH Color Using Red Cabbage Indicator

The pH of a solution tells us whether a solution is acidic, basic, or neutral. On the pH scale, pH values below 7 are acidic, equal to 7 is neutral, and values above 7 are basic. Typically, the pH scale has values between 0 and 14.

pH scale

0 1 2 3 4 5 6 7 8 9 10 11 12 13 14

←——— *acidic* ———→ *neutral* ←——— *basic* ———→

Many natural substances contain dyes that produce distinctive colors at different pH values. By extracting (removing) the dye from red cabbage leaves, a natural indicator can be prepared. Adding the red cabbage solution to solutions of a variety of acids and bases will produce a series of distinctive colors. When the red cabbage solution is added to a test sample, the color produced can be matched to the colors of the pH reference set to determine the pH of the sample. A pH meter can also be used to measure pH.

B. Measuring pH

The concentration (moles/liter, indicated by brackets [ ]) of H_3O^+ or OH^- can be determined from the ionization constant for water (K_w). In pure water, $[H_3O^+] = [OH^-] = 1 \times 10^{-7}$ M.

$$K_w = [H_3O^+][OH^-] = [1 \times 10^{-7}][1 \times 10^{-7}] = 1 \times 10^{-14}$$

If the $[H_3O^+]$ or $[OH^-]$ for an acid or a base is known, the other can be calculated. For example, an acid has a $[H^+] = 1 \times 10^{-4}$ M. We can find the $[OH^-]$ of the solution by solving the K_w expression for $[OH^-]$:

$$[OH^-] = \frac{1 \times 10^{-14}}{[H_3O^+]} = \frac{1 \times 10^{-14}}{1 \times 10^{-4}} = 1 \times 10^{-10} \text{ M}$$

The pH of a solution is a measure of its $[H_3O^+]$. It is defined as the negative log of the hydrogen ion concentration.

$$pH = -\log [H_3O^+]$$

Therefore, a solution with a $[H_3O^+] = 1 \times 10^{-4}$ M has a pH of 4, and is acidic. A solution with a $[H_3O^+] = 1 \times 10^{-11}$ M has a pH of 11, and is basic.

C. Acetic Acid in Vinegar

Vinegar is an aqueous solution of acetic acid, $HC_2H_3O_2$ or CH_3COOH. The amount of acetic acid in a vinegar solution can be determined by neutralizing the acid with a base, in this case NaOH. As shown in the following equation, one mole of acetic acid is neutralized by one mole of NaOH.

$$HC_2H_3O_2 \quad + \quad NaOH \quad \longrightarrow \quad C_2H_3O_2^- \, Na^+ \quad + \quad H_2O$$
Acetic acid   *Base*   *Salt*

A *titration* involves the addition of a specific amount of base required to neutralize an acid in a sample. When all the H^+ (or H_3O^+) from the acid has been neutralized, an indicator in the sample will change color. This change in the indicator color determines the *endpoint,* which signals that the addition of the base should be stopped. The volume of base used to neutralize the acid is then determined. In this experiment, phenolphthalein is the indicator; it changes from colorless in acid to a faint but permanent pink color in base.

Calculating the molarity of acetic acid

Using the average measured volume of the NaOH, and its molarity (on the label), the moles of NaOH used can be calculated.

$$\text{Moles NaOH used} = \text{L NaOH used} \times \frac{\text{moles NaOH}}{\text{L NaOH}}$$

When an acid is completely neutralized, the moles of NaOH are equal to the moles of acetic acid ($HC_2H_3O_2$) present in the sample. This occurs because there are the same number of H^+ and OH^- ions in the reactants:

$$\text{Moles } HC_2H_3O_2 = \text{moles NaOH}$$

Using the moles of acid, the molarity of acetic acid in the 5.0-mL sample of vinegar is calculated.

$$\text{Molarity (M) } HC_2H_3O_2 = \frac{\text{moles } HC_2H_3O_2}{0.0050 \text{ L vinegar}}$$

Calculating the percent (mass/volume) of acetic acid

To calculate the percent (m/v) of $HC_2H_3O_2$ in vinegar, we convert the moles of acetic acid to grams using the molar mass of acetic acid, 60.0 g/mole.

$$\text{g } HC_2H_3O_2 = \text{moles } HC_2H_3O_2 \times \frac{60.0 \text{ g } HC_2H_3O_2}{1 \text{ mole } HC_2H_3O_2}$$

$$\text{Percent (m/v)} = \frac{\text{g } HC_2H_3O_2}{5.0 \text{ mL}} \times 100$$

Lab Information

Time: $1^1/_2$ hr

Comments: Students may be asked to bring a red cabbage to class.

Share test tubes with your lab neighbors to prepare the pH reference solutions.

Observe the color change for the indicators before you do a titration.

Carefully read the markings on the buret.

Tear out the report sheets and place them beside the matching procedures.

Related Topics: Acids, bases, pH, neutralization, titration, percent concentration, molarity

Experimental Procedures

A. pH Color Using Red Cabbage Indicator

Materials: Red cabbage leaves, 400-mL beaker, distilled water, Bunsen burner or hot plate, 150-mL beaker, test tubes, two test tube racks, set of buffers with pH ranging from 1 to 13

Using a 150-mL beaker, obtain 50 mL of cabbage dye indicator. The indicator can be prepared by placing 5 or 6 torn leaves from red cabbage in a 400-mL beaker. Add about 150–200 mL of distilled water to cover the leaves. Heat on a hot plate or using a Bunsen burner, but do not boil. When the solution has attained a dark purple color, turn off the burner and cool.

Preparation of a pH reference set Arrange 13 test tubes in two test tube racks. You may need to combine your test tube set with your neighbor's set. (Your instructor may prepare a pH reference set for the entire class.) Pour 3–4 mL of each buffer in a separate test tube to create a set with pH values of 1–13. **Caution: Low pH values are strongly acidic; high pH values are strongly basic. Work with care.** To each test tube, add 2–3 mL of the *cooled* red cabbage solution. If you wish a deeper color, add more cabbage solution. Describe the colors of the pH solutions. ***Keep this reference set for the next part of the experiment.***

B. Measuring pH

Materials: Shell vials or test tubes, samples to test for pH (shampoo, conditioner, mouthwash, antacids, detergents, fruit juice, vinegar, cleaners, aspirin, etc.), cabbage juice indicator from part A, pH meter, calibration buffers, wash bottle, Kimwipes™

Place 3–4 mL of a sample in a shell vial (or a test tube). Add 2–3 mL of red cabbage solution. Describe the color and compare to the colors of the pH reference set. The pH of the buffer in the reference set that gives the best color match is the pH of the sample. Record. Test several samples.

pH Meter Your instructor will demonstrate the use of the pH meter and calibrate it with a known pH buffer. After you determine the pH of a sample using the red cabbage solution, take the sample to a pH meter, and record the pH. Rinse off the electrode with distilled water.

C. Acetic Acid in Vinegar

Materials: Vinegar (white), two beakers (150 and 250 mL), 250-mL Erlenmeyer flask, 10-mL graduated cylinder (or a 5-mL pipet and bulb), phenolphthalein indicator, 50-mL buret (or 25-mL buret), buret clamp, small funnel to fit buret, 0.1 M NaOH (standardized), white paper or paper towel

C.1 Obtain about 20 mL of vinegar in a small beaker. Record the brand of vinegar and the % acetic acid stated on the label. Using a 10-mL graduated cylinder or a 5.0-mL pipet, transfer 5.0 mL of vinegar to a 250-mL Erlenmeyer flask.

Using a pipet: Place the pipet bulb on the end of the pipet and squeeze the bulb to remove air. Place the tip of the pipet in the vinegar in the beaker and allow the bulb to slowly expand. (If the bulb was squeezed too much, the change in pressure will draw liquid up into the bulb.) When the liquid goes above the volume line, but not into the bulb, carefully remove the bulb and quickly place your second finger (index finger) tightly over the end of the stem. By adjusting the pressure of the index finger, lower the liquid to the etched line that marks the 5.0-mL volume and stop. Lift the pipet with its 5.0 mL of vinegar out of the beaker and let it drain into an Erlenmeyer flask. Touch the tip of the pipet to the wall of the flask to remove the rest of the vinegar. A small amount that remains in the tip has been included in the calibration of the pipet. See Figure 1 for use of a pipet. **Caution: If you are using a pipet, use a suction bulb to draw vinegar into a pipet. Do not pipet by mouth!**

Add about 25 mL of distilled water to increase the volume of the solution for titration. This will not affect your results. Add 2–3 drops of the phenolphthalein indicator to the solution in the flask.

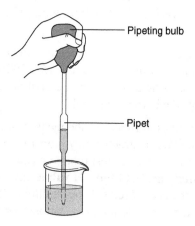

Figure 1 Using a bulb to draw a liquid into a pipet

C.2 Obtain a 50-mL or 25-mL buret and place it in a buret clamp or butterfly clamp as shown in Figure 2. Using a 250-mL beaker, obtain about 100 mL of 0.1 M NaOH solution. (If you are using a 25.0-mL buret, use a 0.2 M NaOH solution.) Record the molarity (M) of the NaOH solution that is stated on the label of the reagent bottle. Rinse the buret with two 5-mL portions of the NaOH solution. Discard the NaOH washings.

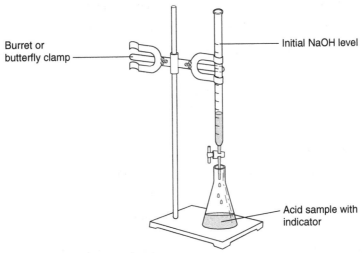

Burret or
butterfly clamp

Initial NaOH level

Acid sample with
indicator

Figure 2 Buret setup for acid–base titration

C.3 Observe the markings on the buret. The top is marked 0.0 mL, and 50.0 mL (or 25.0 mL) is marked at the bottom. Place a small funnel in the top of the buret and carefully pour NaOH into the funnel. Pour slowly as the NaOH fills the buret. Lift the funnel and allow the NaOH to go above the top line (0.0 mL). Slowly open the stopcock and drain NaOH into a waste beaker until the meniscus is at the 0.00 mL line or below. The buret tip should be full of NaOH solution, and free of bubbles. Record the initial buret reading of NaOH.

C.4 Place the flask containing the vinegar solution under the buret on a piece of white paper. (Be sure you added indicator.) Begin to add NaOH to the solution by opening and closing the stopcock with your left hand (if you are right-handed). Swirl the flask with your right hand to mix the acid and the base. At first, the pink color produced by the reaction will disappear quickly. As you near the end-point, the pink color will be more persistent and disappear slowly. *Slow down* the addition of the NaOH to drops at this time. Soon, one drop of NaOH will give a faint, permanent pink color to the sample. *Stop adding NaOH.* You have reached the endpoint of the titration. See Figure 3.

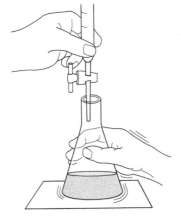

Figure 3 During a titration, the solution in the flask is swirled as NaOH is added to the acid sample.

At the endpoint, record the final buret reading of the NaOH. Fill the buret again. Repeat the titration with new samples of the same brand of vinegar. *Be sure to add water and indicator to each new sample of vinegar.*

Calculations

C.5 Calculate the volume of NaOH used to neutralize the vinegar sample(s).

$$\text{Volume} = \text{Final volume (NaOH)} - \text{initial volume (NaOH)}$$

After the titration of two or three samples of vinegar, calculate the average volume of NaOH used. Total the volumes of NaOH used, and divide by the number of samples you used.

$$\text{mL (average)} \quad \frac{\text{Volume (1)} + \text{Volume (2)} + \text{Volume (3)}}{3}$$

Calculating the molarity of acetic acid

C.6 Convert the volume (average) of NaOH used to a volume in liters (L).

$$L = \text{Average volume (mL) NaOH} \times \frac{1\,L}{1000\,mL}$$

C.7 Calculate the moles of NaOH using the volume (L) and molarity of the NaOH.

$$\text{Moles NaOH used} = \text{L NaOH used} \times \frac{\text{moles NaOH}}{1\,L\,NaOH}$$

C.8 Record the moles of acid present in the vinegar, which are equal to the moles of NaOH used.

$$\text{Moles } HC_2H_3O_2 = \text{moles NaOH used}$$

C.9 Calculate the molarity (M) of the acetic acid ($HC_2H_3O_2$) in the vinegar sample.

$$\text{Molarity (M) } HC_2H_3O_2 = \frac{\text{moles } HC_2H_3O_2}{0.0050\,L\,vinegar}$$

Calculating the percent (mass/volume) of acetic acid

C.10 Using the number of moles of acetic acid, calculate the number of grams of acetic acid in the vinegar sample. The molar mass of acetic acid is 60.0 g/mole.

$$g\,HC_2H_3O_2 = \text{moles } HC_2H_3O_2 \times \frac{60.0\,g\,HC_2H_3O_2}{1\,mole\,HC_2H_3O_2}$$

C.11 Calculate the percent (mass/volume) acetic acid in the vinegar. For an original volume of 5.0 mL of vinegar, the percent is calculated as follows:

$$\text{Percent (m/v)} = \frac{g\,HC_2H_3O_2}{5.0\,mL} \times 100$$

Report Sheet

Date _____ Name _____

Section _____ Team _____

Instructor _____

Pre-Lab Study Questions

1. What does the pH of a solution tell you?

2. What is neutralization?

3. Write an equation for the neutralization of H_2SO_4 by KOH.

4. What is the function of an indicator in a titration?

A. pH Colors Using Red Cabbage Indicator

pH	Colors of Acidic Solutions
1	
2	
3	
4	
5	
6	

pH	Colors of Basic Solutions
8	
9	
10	
11	
12	
13	

pH	Neutral Solution
7	

Report Sheet

B. Measuring pH

Substance	Color with Indicator	pH Using Indicator	pH Using pH Meter	Acidic, Basic, or Neutral?
Household cleaners				
vinegar				
ammonia				
Drinks, juices				
lemon juice				
apple juice				
Detergents, shampoos				
shampoo				
detergent				
hair conditioner				
Health aids				
mouthwash				
antacid				
aspirin				
Other items				

Report Sheet

Questions and Problems

Q.1 Complete the following table:

$[H_3O^+]$	$[OH^-]$	pH	Acidic, Basic, or Neutral?
1×10^{-6}			
		10	
	1×10^{-3}		
			Neutral

Q.2 The label on the shampoo claims that it is pH balanced. What do you think "pH balanced" means?

Q.3 A solution has a $[OH^-] = 1 \times 10^{-5}$ M. What are the $[H_3O^+]$ and the pH of the solution?

Q.4 A sample of 0.0020 mole of HCl is dissolved in water to make a 2000-mL solution. Calculate the molarity of the HCl solution, the $[H_3O^+]$, and the pH. For a strong acid such as HCl, the $[H_3O^+]$ is the same as the molarity of the HCl solution.

$$HCl + H_2O \longrightarrow H_3O^+ + Cl^-$$

Report Sheet

C.   Acetic Acid in Vinegar

C.1   Brand _____   Volume   <u>5.0 mL</u>   (% on label) _____%

C.2   Molarity (M) of NaOH (stated on label)   _____M

		Trial 1	Trial 2	Trial 3
C.3	Initial NaOH level in buret			
C.4	Final NaOH level in buret			
C.5	Volume (mL) of NaOH used			
	Average volume (mL)			
C.6	Average volume in liters (L)			

C.7   Moles of NaOH used in titration   _____ mole NaOH
      (Show calculations.)

C.8   Moles of $HC_2H_3O_2$ neutralized by NaOH   _____ mole $HC_2H_3O_2$

C.9   Molarity of $HC_2H_3O_2$ _____ M $HC_2H_3O_2$
      (Show calculations.)

C.10 Grams $HC_2H_3O_2$ _____ g $HC_2H_3O_2$
      (Show calculations.)

C.11 Percent (m/v) $HC_2H_3O_2$ in vinegar   _____% $HC_2H_3O_2$
      (Show calculations.)

Questions and Problems

Q.5   How many grams of $Mg(OH)_2$ will be needed to neutralize 25 mL of stomach acid if stomach acid is 0.10 M HCl?

Q.6   How many mL of a 0.10 M NaOH solution are needed to neutralize 15 mL of 0.20 M H_3PO_4 solution?

Properties and Structures of Alkanes

Goals

- Observe chemical and physical properties of organic and inorganic compounds.
- Draw formulas for alkanes from their three-dimensional models.
- Write the names of alkanes from their structural formulas.
- Construct models of isomers of alkanes.
- Write the structural formulas for cycloalkanes.

Discussion

A. Color, Odor, and Physical State

Organic compounds are made of carbon and hydrogen, and sometimes oxygen and nitrogen. Of all the elements, only carbon atoms bond to many more carbon atoms, a unique ability that gives rise to many more organic compounds than all the inorganic compounds known today. The covalent bonds in organic compounds and the ionic bonds in inorganic compounds account for several of the differences we will observe in their physical and chemical properties. See Table 1.

Table 1 *Comparing Some Properties of Organic and Inorganic Compounds*

Organic Compounds	Inorganic Compounds
Covalent bonds	Ionic or polar bonds
Soluble in nonpolar solvents, not water	Soluble in water
Low melting and boiling points	High melting and boiling points
Strong, distinct odors	Usually no odor
Poor or nonconductors of electricity	Good conductors of electricity
Flammable	Not flammable

B. Solubility

Typically, inorganic compounds that are ionic are soluble in water, a polar compound, but organic compounds are nonpolar and thus are not soluble in water. However, organic compounds are soluble in organic solvents because they are both nonpolar. A general rule for solubility is that "like dissolves like."

C. Combustion

Many organic compounds react with oxygen, a reaction called *combustion,* to form carbon dioxide and water. Combustion is the reaction that occurs when gasoline burns with oxygen in the engine of a car or when natural gas, methane, burns in a heater or stove. In a combustion reaction, heat is given off; the reaction is exothermic. Equations for the combustion of methane and propane are written as follows:

$$CH_4(g) \ + \ 2O_2(g) \ \longrightarrow \ CO_2(g) \ + \ 2H_2O(g) \ + \ heat$$
methane

$$C_3H_8(g) \ + \ 5O_2(g) \ \longrightarrow \ 3CO_2(g) \ + \ 4H_2O(g) \ + \ heat$$
propane

From *Essential Laboratory Manual for Chemistry: An Introduction to General, Organic, and Biological Chemistry*, Ninth Edition, Karen C. Timberlake. Copyright © 2007 by Pearson Education, Inc. Published by Benjamin Cummings. All rights reserved.

D. Structures of Alkanes

The saturated hydrocarbons represent a group of organic compounds composed of carbon and hydrogen. Alkanes and cycloalkanes are called *saturated* hydrocarbons because their carbon atoms are connected by only single bonds. In each type of alkane, each carbon atom has four valence electrons and must always have four single bonds.

To learn more about the three-dimensional structure of organic compounds, it is helpful to build models using a ball-and-stick model kit. In the kit are wooden (or plastic) balls, which represent the typical elements in organic compounds. Each wooden atom has the correct number of holes drilled for bonds that attach to other atoms. See Table 2.

Table 2 *Elements and Bonds Represented in the Organic Model Kit*

Color	Element	Number of Bonds
Black	carbon	4
Yellow	hydrogen	1
Red	oxygen	2
Green	chlorine	1
Orange	bromine	1
Purple	iodine	1
Blue	nitrogen	3
Bonds		
Sticks, springs		

The first model to build is methane, CH_4, a hydrocarbon consisting of one carbon atom and four hydrogen atoms. The model of methane shows the three-dimensional shape, a tetrahedron, around a carbon atom.

| Three-dimensional structure | Complete structural formula | Condensed structural formula |

To represent this model on paper, its shape is flattened, and the carbon atom is shown attached to four hydrogen atoms. This type of formula is called a *complete structural formula*. However, it is more convenient to use a shortened version called a *condensed structural formula*. To write a condensed formula, the hydrogen atoms are grouped with their carbon atom. The number of hydrogen atoms is written as a subscript. The complete structural formula and the condensed structural formula for C_2H_6 are shown below:

Complete structural formula   Condensed structural formula

Names of Alkanes

The names of alkanes all end with *-ane*. The names of organic compounds are based on the names of the alkane family. See Table 3.

Table 3 *Names and Formulas of the First Ten Alkanes*

Name	Formula	Name	Formula
Methane	CH_4	Hexane	$CH_3CH_2CH_2CH_2CH_2CH_3$
Ethane	CH_3CH_3	Heptane	$CH_3CH_2CH_2CH_2CH_2CH_2CH_3$
Propane	$CH_3CH_2CH_3$	Octane	$CH_3CH_2CH_2CH_2CH_2CH_2CH_2CH_3$
Butane	$CH_3CH_2CH_2CH_3$	Nonane	$CH_3CH_2CH_2CH_2CH_2CH_2CH_2CH_2CH_3$
Pentane	$CH_3CH_2CH_2CH_2CH_3$	Decane	$CH_3CH_2CH_2CH_2CH_2CH_2CH_2CH_2CH_2CH_3$

E. Isomers

Isomers are present when a molecular formula can represent two or more different structural (or condensed) formulas. One structure cannot be converted to the other without breaking and forming new bonds. The isomers have different physical and chemical properties. One of the reasons for the vast array of organic compounds is the phenomenon of isomerism.

Isomers of C_4H_{10}

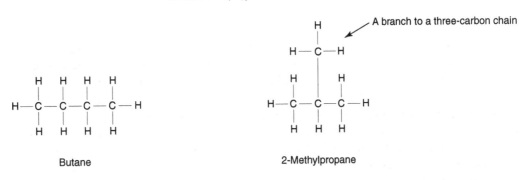

Butane

2-Methylpropane

A branch to a three-carbon chain

F. Cycloalkanes

In a cycloalkane, an alkane has a cyclic or ring structure. There are no end carbon atoms. The structural formula of a cycloalkane indicates all of the carbon and hydrogen atoms. The condensed formula groups the hydrogen atoms with each of the carbon atoms. Another type of notation called the *geometric* structure is often used to depict a cycloalkane by showing only the bonds that outline the geometric shape of the compound. For example, the geometric shape of cyclopropane is a triangle, and the geometric shape of cyclobutane is a square. Examples of the various structural formulas for cyclobutane are shown below.

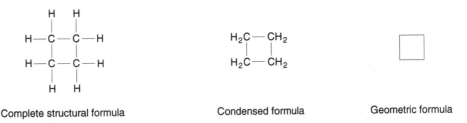

Complete structural formula   Condensed formula   Geometric formula

Lab Information

Time:	$1\frac{1}{2}$ hr
Comments:	Tear out the report sheets and place them next to the matching procedures. ***Organic compounds are extremely flammable! Use of the Bunsen burner is prohibited.***
Related Topics:	Organic compounds, hydrocarbons, solubility, combustion, alkane, cycloalkane, complete structural formula, condensed structural formula, isomers, naming alkanes

Properties and Structures of Alkanes

Experimental Procedures   Wear your safety goggles!

A. Color, Odor, and Physical State *(This may be a lab display.)*

Materials: Test tubes (6), test tube rack, spatulas, NaCl(s), KI(s), toluene, benzoic acid, cyclohexane, water, chemistry handbook

Place each substance into a separate test tube: a few crystals of NaCl, KI, and benzoic acid, and 10 drops each of cyclohexane, toluene, and water. Or if a display is available, observe the samples in a test tube rack in the hood. Record the formula, physical state (solid, liquid, or gas), and odor of each one. To check for odor, first take a breath and hold it while you gently fan the air above the test tube toward you. Look up the melting point of each compound using a chemistry handbook. Record. State the types of bonds in each as ionic or covalent. Identify each as an organic or inorganic compound.

B. Solubility *(This may be a demonstration or lab display.)*

Materials: Test tubes, spatulas, NaCl(s), toluene, cyclohexane

Work in the hood: Be sure to work with the compounds such as cyclohexane in ventilation hoods, and then dispose of them in the proper waste containers. Place 10 drops of cyclohexane and 10 drops of water in a test tube. Record your observations. Identify the upper layer and the lower layer.

Place a few crystals of NaCl in one test tube and 10 drops of toluene in another test tube. To each sample, add 15 drops of cyclohexane, a nonpolar solvent. Shake gently or tap the bottom of the test tube to mix. Record whether each substance is soluble (S) or insoluble (I) in cyclohexane.

Repeat the experiment with the two substances, but this time add 15 drops of water, a polar solvent. Record whether each substance is soluble (S) or insoluble (I) in water. Identify each substance as an organic or inorganic compound.

> ## Dispose of organic substances in the proper waste container.

C. Combustion *(This may be a demonstration by your instructor.)*

Materials: 2 evaporating dishes, spatulas, wood splints, NaCl(s), cyclohexane

Work in the hood: Place a small amount (pea-size) of NaCl in an evaporating dish set in an iron ring. Ignite a splint and hold the flame to the NaCl. Record whether the substance melts, changes color, or burns. Repeat the experiment using 5 drops of cyclohexane instead of NaCl. If the substance burns, note the color of the flame. Identify each as an organic or inorganic compound.

D. Structures of Alkanes

Materials: Organic model kit

D.1 Using an organic model kit, construct a ball-and-stick model of a molecule of methane, CH_4. Place wooden dowels in all the holes in the carbon atom (black). Attach hydrogen (yellow) atoms to each. Draw the three-dimensional (tetrahedral) shape of methane. Write the complete structural formula and the condensed structural formula of methane.

D.2 Make a model of ethane, C_2H_6. Observe that the tetrahedral shape is maintained for each carbon atom in the structure. Write the complete structural and condensed structural formulas for ethane.

D.3 Make a model of propane, C_3H_8. Write the complete structural and condensed structural formulas for propane.

E. Isomers

Materials: Organic model kit, chemistry handbook

E.1   The molecular formula of butane is C_4H_{10}. Construct a model of butane by connecting four carbon atoms in a chain. Draw its complete and condensed structural formulas.

E.2   Make an isomer of C_4H_{10}. Remove an end -CH_3 group and attach it to the center carbon atom. Complete the end of the chain with a hydrogen atom. Write its complete and condensed structural formulas.

E.3   Obtain a chemistry handbook. For each isomer, find the molar mass, melting point, boiling point, and density.

E.4   Make models of the three isomers of C_5H_{12}. Make the continuous-chain isomer first. Draw the complete structural and condensed structural formulas for each. Name each isomer.

E.5   Obtain a chemistry handbook, and find the molar mass, melting point, boiling point, and density of each structural isomer.

F. Cycloalkanes

Materials: Organic model kit

F.1   Use the springs in the model kits to make a model of the cycloalkane with three carbon atoms. Write the complete structural and condensed structural formulas. Draw the geometric formula and name this compound.

F.2   Use the springs in the model kits to make models of a cycloalkane with four carbon atoms, and one with five carbon atoms. Draw the complete structural and condensed structural formulas. Draw the geometric formula and give the name for each.

Report Sheet

Date _____   Name _____

Section _____   Team _____

Instructor _____

Pre-Lab Study Questions

1. Would you expect an organic compound to be soluble in water? Why?

2. Which is more flammable: an organic or inorganic compound?

3. How does a complete structural formula differ from a condensed structural formula?

4. If isomers of an alkane have the same molecular formula, how do they differ?

A. Color, Odor, and Physical State

Name	Formula	Physical State	Odor	Melting Point	Type of Bonds?	Organic or Inorganic?
Sodium chloride						
Cyclohexane	C_6H_{12}					
Potassium iodide						
Benzoic acid	$C_7H_6O_2$					
Toluene	C_7H_8					
Water						

B. Solubility

In the mixture, water is the _____ layer and cyclohexane is the _____ layer.

Solute	Solubility in Cyclohexane	Solubility in Water	Organic or Inorganic?
NaCl			
Toluene			

Report Sheet

C. Combustion

Compound	Flammable (Color of Flame)	Not Flammable	Organic or Inorganic?
NaCl			
Cyclohexane			

From your observations of the chemical and physical properties of alkanes as organic compounds, complete the following table:

Property	Organic Compounds	Inorganic Compounds
Elements		
Bonding		
Melting points		
Strong odors		
Flammability		
Solubility		

Questions and Problems

Q.1 Describe three properties you can use to distinguish between organic and inorganic compounds.

Q.2 A white solid has no odor, is soluble in water, and is not flammable. Would you expect it to be an organic or an inorganic substance? Why?

Q.3 A clear liquid with a gasoline-like odor forms a layer when added to water. Would you expect it to be an organic or an inorganic substance? Why?

Report Sheet

D. Structures of Alkanes

D.1 Structure of methane		
Tetrahedral shape	Complete structural formula	Condensed structural formula

D.2 Structure of ethane	
Complete structural formula	Condensed structural formula

D.3 Structure of propane	
Complete structural formula	Condensed structural formula

Questions and Problems

Q.4 Write the correct name of the following alkanes:

a. $CH_3CH_2CH_3$ _____

b.
$$\begin{array}{c} CH_3 \\ | \\ CH_3CH_2CHCHCH_3 \\ | \\ CH_3 \end{array}$$
_____

c.
$$\begin{array}{c} CH_3 \quad CH_3 \\ | \qquad | \\ CH_3-CH-CH-CH_3 \end{array}$$
_____

Report Sheet

Q.5 Write the condensed formulas for the following:
  a. hexane

  b. 2,3-dimethylpentane

E. Isomers

E.1 Butane C_4H_{10}	
Complete structural formula	Condensed structural formula
E.2 2-Methylpropane	
Complete structural formula	Condensed structural formul

E.3 Physical Properties of Isomers of C_4H_{10}				
Isomer	**Molar Mass**	**Melting Point**	**Boiling Point**	**Density**
Butane				
2-Methylpropane (isobutane)				

Questions and Problems

Q.6 In E.3, what physical property is identical for the two isomers of C_4H_{10}?

Q.7 What physical properties are different for the isomers? Explain.

Report Sheet

E.4 Isomers of C_5H_{12}	
Complete structural formula	Condensed structural formula
Name:	
Complete structural formula	Condensed structural formula
Name:	
Complete structural formula	Condensed structural formula
Name:	

E.5 Physical Properties of Isomers of C_5H_{12}				
Isomer	**Molar Mass**	**Melting Point**	**Boiling Point**	**Density**
Pentane				
2-Methylbutane				
2,2-Dimethylpropane				

Properties and Structures of Alkanes

Report Sheet

Questions and Problems

Q.8 Write the condensed formulas for the isomers of C_6H_{14}.

F. Cycloalkanes

Complete Structural Formula	Condensed Structural Formula	Geometric Formula
F.1 Three carbon atoms		
Name:		
F.2 Four carbon atoms		
Name:		
Five carbon atoms		
Name:		

Alcohols, Aldehydes, and Ketones

Goals

- Determine chemical and physical properties of alcohols, aldehydes, and ketones.
- Classify an alcohol as primary, secondary, or tertiary.
- Perform a chemical test to distinguish between the classes of alcohols.
- Write the formulas of the oxidation products of alcohols.
- Perform chemical tests to distinguish between aldehydes and ketones.

Discussion

A. Structures of Alcohols and Phenol

Alcohols are organic compounds that contain the hydroxyl group (–OH). The simplest alcohol is methanol. Ethanol is found in alcoholic beverages and preservatives, and is used as a solvent. 2-Propanol, also known as rubbing alcohol, is found in astringents and perfumes.

$$CH_3OH$$

Methanol
(methyl alcohol)

$$\overset{\overset{\textstyle OH}{|}}{CH_3CHCH_3}$$

2-Propanol
(isopropyl alcohol)

$$CH_3CH_2OH$$

Ethanol
(ethyl alcohol)

A benzene ring with a hydroxyl group is known as phenol. Concentrated solutions of phenol are caustic and cause burns. However, derivatives of phenol, such as thymol, are used as antiseptics and are sometimes found in cough drops.

Phenol

Thymol
(2-isopropyl-5-methylphenol)

Classification of Alcohols

In a primary (1°) alcohol, the carbon atom attached to the –OH group is bonded to one other carbon atom. In a secondary (2°) alcohol, it is attached to two carbon atoms and in a tertiary (3°) alcohol to three carbon atoms.

Ethanol
primary (1°) alcohol

2-Propanol
secondary (2°) alcohol

2-Methyl-2-Propanol
tertiary (3°) alcohol

From *Essential Laboratory Manual for Chemistry: An Introduction to General, Organic, and Biological Chemistry*, Ninth Edition, Karen C. Timberlake. Copyright © 2007 by Pearson Education, Inc. Published by Benjamin Cummings. All rights reserved.

B. Properties of Alcohols and Phenol

The polarity of the hydroxyl group (–OH) makes alcohols with four or fewer carbon atoms soluble in water because they can form hydrogen bonds. However, in longer-chain alcohols, a large hydrocarbon section makes them insoluble in water.

C. Oxidation of Alcohols

Primary and secondary alcohols are easily oxidized. An oxidation consists of removing an H from the –OH group and another H from the C atom attached to the –OH group. Tertiary alcohols do not undergo oxidation because there are no H atoms on that C atom. Primary and secondary alcohols can be distinguished from tertiary alcohols using a solution with chromate, CrO_4^{2-}. An oxidation has occurred when the orange color of the chromate solution turns green.

D. Properties of Aldehydes and Ketones

Aldehydes and ketones both contain the carbonyl group. In an aldehyde, the carbonyl group has a hydrogen atom attached; the aldehyde functional group occurs at the end of the carbon chain. In a ketone, the carbonyl group is located between two of the carbon atoms within the chain.

Many aldehydes and ketones have sharp odors. If you have taken a biology class, you may have noticed the sharp odor of Formalin™, which is a solution of formaldehyde. When you remove finger-nail polish, you may notice the strong odor of acetone, the simplest ketone, which is used as the solvent. Aromatic aldehydes have a variety of odors. Benzaldehyde, the simplest aromatic aldehyde, has an odor of almonds.

Formaldehyde

Benzaldehyde

E. Iodoform Test for Methyl Ketones

Ketones containing a methyl group attached to the carbonyl give a reaction with iodine (I_2) in a NaOH solution. The reaction produces solid, yellow iodoform, CHI_3. Iodoform, which has a strong medicinal odor, is used as an antiseptic.

$$CH_3-\overset{O}{\underset{||}{C}}-CH_3 \ + \ 3I_2 \ + \ 4NaOH \ \longrightarrow \ CH_3-\overset{O}{\underset{||}{C}}-O^-Na^+ \ + \ CHI_3 \ + \ 3NaI \ + \ 3H_2O$$

Methyl ketone   Iodine   Iodoform

(red)   (yellow)

F. Oxidation of Aldehydes and Ketones

Aldehydes are oxidized using Benedict's solution, which contains cupric ion, Cu^{2+}. Because ketones cannot oxidize, this test can distinguish aldehydes from ketones. In the oxidation reaction, the blue-green Cu^{2+} is reduced to cuprous ion (Cu^+), which forms a reddish-orange precipitate of Cu_2O.

$$CH_3-\overset{O}{\underset{||}{C}}-H \ + \ 2Cu^{2+} \ \longrightarrow \ CH_3-\overset{O}{\underset{||}{C}}-OH \ + \ Cu_2O(s)$$

Aldehyde   Blue   Red-orange

$$CH_3-\overset{O}{\underset{||}{C}}-CH_3 \ + \ 2Cu^{2+} \ \longrightarrow \ \text{No reaction (stays blue)}$$

Ketone   Blue

Lab Information

Time: 2–2$^{1}/_{2}$ hr

Comments: Be careful when you work with chromate solution. It contains concentrated acid. Do not use burners in the lab when you work with flammable organic compounds. Tear out the report sheets and place them beside the matching procedures.

Related Topics: Alcohols, classification of alcohols, solubility of alcohols in water, phenols, oxidation of alcohols, aldehydes, ketones, oxidation of aldehydes

Experimental Procedures

GOGGLES MUST BE WORN

A. Structures of Alcohols and Phenol

Materials: Organic model kits

Observe the models or obtain an organic model kit and construct models of ethanol, 2-propanol, and *t*-butyl alcohol (2-methyl-2-propanol). Write the condensed structural formula of each. Write the condensed structural formula for phenol. Classify each alcohol as a primary, secondary, or tertiary alcohol.

B. Properties of Alcohols and Phenol

Materials: 5 test tubes, pH paper, stirring rod, ethanol, 2-propanol, *t*-butyl alcohol (2-methyl-2-propanol), cyclohexanol, 20% phenol

Odor Place 5 drops of each of the alcohols and of phenol into separate test tubes. *Avoid skin contact with phenol.* Carefully detect the odor of each. Hold your breath as you gently fan some fumes from the top of the test tube toward you.

Solubility in water Add about 2 mL of water (40 drops) to each test tube. Shake and determine whether each alcohol is soluble or not. If the substance is soluble in water, you will see a clear solution with no separate layers. If it is insoluble, a cloudy mixture or separate layer will form. Record your observations.

Acidity Obtain a container of pH paper. Place a stirring rod in one of the alcohols and touch a drop to the pH paper. Compare the color of the paper with the chart on the container to determine the pH of the solution. Record.

DISPOSE OF ORGANIC SUBSTANCES IN DESIGNATED WASTE CONTAINERS!

C. Oxidation of Alcohols

Materials: 4 test tubes, ethanol, 2-propanol, 2-methyl-2-propanol (*t*-butyl alcohol), cyclohexanol, 2% chromate solution

C.1 Place 8 drops of the alcohols in separate test tubes. Carefully add 2 drops of chromate solution to each. Look for a color change in the chromate solution as you add it to the sample. If the orange color turns to green in 1–2 minutes, oxidation of the alcohol has taken place. If the color remains orange, no reaction has occurred. If a test tube becomes hot, place it in a beaker of ice-cold water. Record your observations. **Caution: Chromate solution contains concentrated H_2SO_4, which is corrosive.**

C.2 Draw the condensed structural formula of each alcohol.

C.3 Classify each alcohol as primary (1°), secondary (2°), or tertiary (3°).

C.4 Draw the condensed structural formulas of the products where oxidation occurred. When there is no change in color, no oxidation took place. Write "no reaction" (NR).

D. Properties of Aldehydes and Ketones

Materials: Chemistry handbook, test tubes, droppers, 5- or 10-mL graduated cylinder, acetone, benzaldehyde, camphor, vanillin, cinnamaldehyde, 2,3-butanedione, propionaldehyde, cyclohexanone

Odors of Aldehydes and Ketones

D.1 Carefully detect the odor of samples of acetone, benzaldehyde, camphor, vanillin, cinnamaldehyde, and 2,3-butanedione.

D.2 Draw their condensed structural formulas. You may need a chemistry handbook or a *Merck Index*. Identify each as a ketone or aldehyde.

Solubility of Aldehydes and Ketones

D.3 Place 2 mL of water in each of 4 separate test tubes. Add 5 drops of propionaldehyde (propanal), benzaldehyde, acetone, and cyclohexanone. Record your observations. ***Save the samples for part E.***

E. Iodoform Test for Methyl Ketones

Materials: Test tubes from part D.3, dropper, 10% NaOH, warm water bath, and iodine test reagent

Using the test tubes from part D.3, add 10 drops of 10% NaOH to each. Warm the tubes in a warm water bath to 50–60°C. Add 20 drops of iodine test reagent. Look for the formation of a yellow solid precipitate. Record your results.

F. Oxidation of Aldehydes and Ketones

Materials: Test tubes, propionaldehyde (propanal), benzaldehyde, acetone, cyclohexanone, Benedict's reagent, droppers, boiling water bath

Place 10 drops of propionaldehyde (propanal), benzaldehyde, acetone, and cyclohexanone in separate test tubes. Label. Add 5 mL of Benedict's reagent to each test tube. Place the test tubes in the boiling water bath for 5 minutes. The appearance of the red-orange color of Cu_2O indicates that oxidation has occurred. Moderate amounts of Cu_2O will blend with the blue Cu^{2+} solution to form green or rust color. Record your observations. Identify the compounds that gave an oxidation reaction.

Report Sheet

Date _____   Name _____

Section _____   Team _____

Instructor _____

Pre-Lab Study Questions

1. What is the functional group of an alcohol, aldehyde, and ketone?

2. Why are some alcohols soluble in water?

3. How are alcohols classified?

A. Structures of Alcohols and Phenols

Ethanol	2-Propanol
Classification:	
2-Methyl-2-propanol	Phenol
Classification:	

Report Sheet

Questions and Problems

Q.1 Write the structures and classifications of the following alcohols:

1-Pentanol	3-Pentanol
Cyclopentanol	1-Methylcyclopentanol

B. Properties of Alcohols and Phenols

Alcohol	Odor	Soluble in Water?	pH
Ethanol			
2-Propanol			
2-Methyl-2-propanol			
Cyclohexanol			
Phenol			

Report Sheet

C. Oxidation of Alcohols

Alcohol	C.1 Color Change with CrO_4^{2-}	C.2 Condensed Structural Formula	C.3 Classification	C.4 Oxidation Product (if reaction takes place)
Ethanol				
2-Propanol				
2-Methyl-2-propanol				
Cyclohexanol				

Questions and Problems

Q.2 Write the product of the following reactions (if no reaction, write NR):

a.
$$CH_3CH_2CH_2OH \xrightarrow{[O]}$$

b.
$$\underset{\underset{\displaystyle CH_3CHCH_2CH_3}{|}}{OH} \xrightarrow{[O]}$$

c.
cyclohexanol with OH $\xrightarrow{[O]}$

Report Sheet

D. Properties of Aldehydes and Ketones

	D.1 **Odor**	D.2 **Condensed Structural Formula**	**Aldehyde or Ketone?**
Acetone			
Benzaldehyde			
Camphor			
Vanillin			
Cinnamaldehyde			
2,3-Butanedione			

Report Sheet

Questions and Problems

Q.3 What aldehyde or ketone might be present in the following everyday products?

Artificial butter flavor in popcorn _____

Almond-flavored cookies _____

Candies with cinnamon flavor _____

Nail polish remover _____

D., E., and F.   Solubility, Iodoform, and Oxidation of Aldehydes and Ketones

	D.3 **Solubility** Soluble in water?	E. **Iodoform Test** Methyl ketone present?	F. **Benedict's Test** Oxidation occurred?
Propionaldehyde			
Benzaldehyde			
Acetone			
Cyclohexanone			

Questions and Problems

Q.4 Complete the following with the word *soluble or insoluble:*

Aldehydes and ketones containing one to four carbon atoms are _____ in water.

Aldehydes and ketones containing five or more carbon atoms are _____ in water.

Report Sheet

Q.5 Indicate the test results for each of the following compounds in the iodoform test and in the Benedict's test:

	Iodoform Test	Benedict's Test
O $\\|$ $CH_3CCH_2CH_3$		
O $\\|$ CH_3CH		
O $\\|$ $CH_3CH_2CCH_2CH_3$		
$O \quad O$ $\\| \quad \\|$ CH_3CCH_2CH		

Q.6 Two compounds, A and B, have the formula of C_3H_6O. Determine their condensed structural formulas and names using the following test results.

a. Compound A forms a red-orange precipitate with Benedict's reagent, but does not react with iodoform.

b. Compound B forms a yellow solid in the iodoform test, but does not react with Benedict's reagent.

Carboxylic Acids and Esters

Goals

- Write the structural formulas of carboxylic acids and esters.
- Determine the solubility and acidity of carboxylic acids and their salts.
- Write equations for neutralization and esterification of acids.
- Prepare esters and identify their characteristic odors.
- Use an esterification reaction to synthesize aspirin.

Discussion

A. Carboxylic Acids and Their Salts

A salad dressing made of oil and vinegar tastes tart because it contains vinegar, which is known as acetic acid (ethanoic acid). The sour taste of fruits such as lemons is due to acids such as citric acid. Face creams contain alpha hydroxy acids such as glycolic acid. All these acids are carboxylic acids, which contain the carboxyl group: a carbonyl group attached to a hydroxyl group. A dicarboxylic acid such as malonic acid, found in apples, has two carboxylic acid functional groups. The carboxylic acid of benzene is called benzoic acid.

Ionization of Carboxylic Acids in Water

Carboxylic acids are weak acids because the carboxylic acid group ionizes slightly in water to give a proton and a carboxylate ion. However, like the alcohols, the polarity of the carboxylic acid group makes acids with one to four carbon atoms soluble in water. Acids with two or more carboxyl groups (diacids) are more soluble in water.

From *Essential Laboratory Manual for Chemistry: An Introduction to General, Organic, and Biological Chemistry*, Ninth Edition, Karen C. Timberlake. Copyright © 2007 by Pearson Education, Inc. Published by Benjamin Cummings. All rights reserved.

Carboxylic Acids and Esters

Neutralization of Carboxylic Acids

An important feature of carboxylic acids is their neutralization by bases such as sodium hydroxide to form carboxylate salts and water. We saw in an earlier experiment that neutralization is the reaction of an acid with a base to give a salt and water. Even insoluble carboxylic acids with five or more carbon atoms can be neutralized to give corresponding salts that are usually soluble in water. For this reason, acids used in food products or medications are in their soluble salt form rather than the acid itself.

$$HX \quad + \quad NaOH \quad \longrightarrow \quad Na^+X^- \quad + \quad H_2O$$

Acid	Base	Salt	Water

$$CH_3-\overset{\overset{\displaystyle O}{\|}}{C}-OH \quad + \quad NaOH \quad \longrightarrow \quad CH_3-\overset{\overset{\displaystyle O}{\|}}{C}-O^-Na^+ \quad + \quad H_2O$$

Acetic acid   Sodium acetate
(a carboxylate salt)

B. Esters

Carboxylic acids may have tart or unpleasant odors, but many esters have pleasant flavors and fragrant odors. Octyl acetate gives oranges their characteristic odor and flavor; pear flavor is due to pentyl acetate. The flavor and odor of raspberries come from isobutyl formate.

$$CH_3(CH_2)_7O-\overset{\overset{\displaystyle O}{\|}}{C}-CH_3 \qquad CH_3(CH_2)_4-O-\overset{\overset{\displaystyle O}{\|}}{C}-CH_3 \qquad CH_3-\overset{\overset{\displaystyle CH_3}{|}}{C}HCH_2-O-\overset{\overset{\displaystyle O}{\|}}{C}-H$$

Octyl acetate   Pentyl acetate   Isobutyl formate
(oranges)   (pears)   (raspberries)

An ester of salicylic acid is methyl salicylate, which gives the flavor and odor of oil of wintergreen used in candies and ointments for sore muscles. When salicylic acid reacts with acetic anhydride, acetylsalicylic acid (ASA) is formed, which is aspirin, widely used to reduce fever and inflammation.

Methyl salicylate
(wintergreen)

Acetylsalicylic acid
(aspirin)

Esterification and Hydrolysis of Methyl Salicylate

In a reaction called *esterification*, the carboxylic acid group combines with the hydroxyl group of an alcohol. The reaction, which takes place in the presence of an acid, produces an ester and water.

Esterification ⟶

$$CH_3-\overset{\overset{\displaystyle O}{\|}}{C}-OH \quad + \quad HO-(CH_2)_4-CH_3 \underset{}{\overset{H^+}{\rightleftharpoons}} CH_3-\overset{\overset{\displaystyle O}{\|}}{C}-O-(CH_2)_4-CH_3 \quad + \quad H_2O$$

Acetic acid   1-Pentanol   Pentyl acetate (pear flavor)

⟵ Hydrolysis

The reverse reaction, hydrolysis, occurs when an acid catalyst and water cause the decomposition of an ester to yield the carboxylic acid and alcohol. The ester product is favored when an excess of acid or alcohol is used; hydrolysis is favored when more water is used.

C. Preparation of Aspirin

In the 18th century, an extract of willow bark was found useful in reducing fevers (antipyretic) and relieving pain and inflammation. Although salicylic acid was effective at reducing fever and pain, it damaged the mucous membranes of the mouth and esophagus, and caused hemorrhaging of the stomach lining. At the turn of the century, scientists at the Bayer Company in Germany noted that salicylic acid contained a phenol group that might cause the damage. They decided to modify salicylic acid by forming an ester with a two-carbon acetyl group. The resulting substance was acetylsalicylic acid, or ASA, which we call aspirin. Aspirin acts by inhibiting the formation of prostaglandins, 20-carbon acids that form at the site of an injury and cause inflammation and pain.

In commercial aspirin products, a small amount of acetylsalicylic acid (300 mg to 400 mg) is bound together with a starch binder and sometimes caffeine and buffers to make an aspirin tablet. The basic conditions in the small intestine break down the acetylsalicylic acid to yield salicylic acid, which is absorbed into the bloodstream. The addition of a buffer reduces the irritation caused by the carboxylic acid group of the aspirin molecule.

Aspirin (acetylsalicylic acid) can be prepared from acetic acid and the hydroxyl group on salicylic acid. However, this is a slow reaction. The ester forms rapidly when acetic anhydride is used to provide the acetyl group. *The aspirin you will prepare in this experiment is impure and must not be taken internally!*

| Salicylic acid (138 g/mole) | Acetic anhydride | Aspirin (acetylsalicylic acid) (180 g/mole) | Acetic acid |

Using the following equation, the maximum amount (yield) of aspirin that is possible from 2.00 g of salicylic acid can be calculated.

$$2.00 \text{ g salicylic acid} \times \frac{1 \text{ mole salicylic acid}}{138 \text{ g}} \times \frac{1 \text{ mole aspirin}}{1 \text{ mole salicyclic acid}} \times \frac{180 \text{ g}}{1 \text{ mole aspirin}}$$

$$= 2.61 \text{ g aspirin (possible)}$$

Suppose the total amount of aspirin you obtain has a mass of 2.25 g. A percentage yield can be calculated as follows:

$$\% \text{ Yield} = \frac{\text{g aspirin obtained}}{\text{g aspirin calculated}} \times 100 = \frac{2.25 \text{ g}}{2.61 \text{ g}} \times 100 = 86.2\% \text{ yield of aspirin product}$$

Lab Information

Time: 2 hr

Comments: When noting odors, hold your breath and fan across the top of a test tube to detect the odor. The formation of esters requires concentrated acid. Use carefully.

In the synthesis of aspirin, the product is not pure and must not be taken internally.

Tear out the report sheets and place them beside the matching procedure.

Related Topics: Carboxylic acids, esters, ionization of carboxylic acids, neutralization, esterification

Experimental Procedures

BE SURE YOU WEAR YOUR SAFETY GOGGLES!

A. Carboxylic Acids and Their Salts

Materials: Test tubes, glacial acetic acid, benzoic acid(*s*), spatula, pH paper, red and blue litmus paper, stirring rod, 400-mL beaker, hot plate or Bunsen burner, 10% NaOH, 10% HCl

A.1 Write the structural formulas for acetic acid and benzoic acid.

A.2 Place about 2 mL of water in two test tubes. Add 5 drops of acetic acid to one test tube and a small amount of benzoic solid (enough to cover the tip of a spatula) to the other. Tap the sides of the test tubes to mix or stir with a stirring rod. Identify the acid that dissolves.

A.3 Test the pH of each carboxylic acid by dipping a stirring rod into the solution, then touching it to a piece of pH paper. Compare the color on the paper with the color chart on the container and report the pH.

A.4 Place the test tube of benzoic acid (solid should be present) in a hot water bath and heat for 5 minutes. Describe the effect of heating on the solubility of acid. Allow the test tube to cool. Record your observations.

A.5 Add about 10 drops of NaOH to the test tube containing benzoic acid until a drop of the solution turns red litmus paper blue. Observe the contents of the test tube. Write the structure of the sodium salt formed.

B. Esters

Materials: Organic model set, test tubes, hot plate or Bunsen burner, 400-mL beaker, stirring rod, spatula, small beaker, methanol, 1-pentanol, 1-octanol, benzyl alcohol, 1-propanol, salicylic acid(*s*), glacial acetic acid, H_3PO_4 in a dropper bottle

B.1 Make a model of acetic acid and methyl alcohol. Remove the components of water and form an ester bond to give methyl acetate. Write the equation for the formation of the ester.

B.2 As assigned, prepare one of the mixtures listed by placing 3 mL of the alcohol in a test tube and label it with the mixture number. Add 2 mL of a carboxylic acid or the amount of solid that covers the tip of a spatula. Write the condensed structural formulas for the alcohols and carboxylic acids.

Mixture	Alcohol	Carboxylic Acid
1	Methanol	Salicylic acid
2	1-Pentanol	Acetic acid
3	1-Octanol	Acetic acid
4	Benzyl alcohol	Acetic acid
5	1-Propanol	Acetic acid

Use care in dispensing glacial acetic acid. It can cause burns and blisters on the skin.

B.3 With the test tube pointed away from you, *cautiously* add 15 drops of concentrated phosphoric acid, H_3PO_4. Stir. Place the test tube in a boiling water bath for 15 minutes. Remove the test tube and *cautiously* fan the vapors toward you. Record the odors you detect such as pear, banana, orange, raspberry, or oil of wintergreen (spearmint). For a stronger odor, place 15 mL of hot water in a small beaker and pour the ester solution into the hot water.

If specified by your instructor, repeat the esterification with other mixtures of alcohol and carboxylic acid. Note the odors of esters produced by other students. Write the condensed structural formulas and names of the esters produced. *Dispose of the ester products as instructed*.

C. Preparation of Aspirin

Materials: 125-mL Erlenmeyer flask, 400-mL beaker, hot plate or Bunsen burner, ice, salicylic acid, acetic anhydride, 5- or 10-mL graduated cylinder, stirring rod, pan or large beaker, dropper, 85% H_3PO_4 in a dropper bottle, Büchner filtration apparatus, filter paper, spatula, watch glass

C.1 Weigh a 125-mL Erlenmeyer flask. Add 2 g of salicylic acid and reweigh. *Working in the hood, carefully* add 5 mL of acetic anhydride to the flask.

Caution: Acetic anhydride is irritating to the nose and sinuses. Handle carefully.

Slowly add 10 drops of 85% phosphoric acid, H_3PO_4. Stir the mixture with a stirring rod. Place the flask and its contents in a boiling water bath and stir until all the solid dissolves.

Remove the flask from the hot water and let it cool. **Working in the hood, cautiously** add 20 drops of water to the cooled mixture.

KEEP YOUR FACE AWAY FROM THE TOP OF THE FLASK.
ACETIC ACID VAPORS ARE IRRITATING.

When the reaction is complete, add 50 mL of cold water. Cool the mixture by placing the flask in an ice bath for 10 minutes. Stir. Crystals of aspirin should form. If no crystals appear, gently scratch the sides of the flask with a stirring rod.

Collecting the Aspirin Crystals

Some Büchner filtration apparatuses should be set up in the lab. Add a piece of filter paper. Place the funnel in the filter flask, making sure that its neck fits snugly in a rubber washer. See Figure 1. Moisten the filter paper. Turn on the water aspirator and pour the aspirin product onto the filter paper in the Büchner funnel. Push down gently on the funnel to create the suction needed to pull the water off the aspirin product. The aspirin crystals will collect on the filter paper.

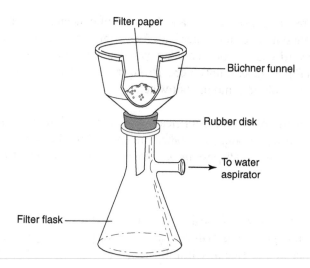

Figure 1 Apparatus for suction filtration with a Büchner funnel

Use a spatula to transfer any crystals left in the flask. Rinse the inside of the flask with 10 mL of cold water to transfer all the crystals to the funnel. Wash the aspirin crystals on the filter paper with two 10-mL portions of cold water.

Spread the aspirin crystals out on the filter paper and draw air through the funnel. This helps dry the crystals. Turn off the water aspirator and use a spatula to lift and transfer the filter paper and aspirin to a paper towel. Don't touch it; it may still contain acid. Allow the crystals to air dry.

C.2 Weigh a clean, dry watch glass. Transfer the crude aspirin crystals to the watch glass and reweigh.

Calculations

C.3 Calculate the mass of salicylic acid.

C.4 Calculate the maximum yield of aspirin possible from the salicylic acid.

C.5 Calculate the mass of the crude aspirin you collected.

C.6 Calculate the percentage yield of aspirin.

C.7 If a melting point apparatus is available, determine the melting points of the aspirin product. Pure aspirin has a melting point of 135°C. Salicylic acid melts at 157–159°C. Compare the melting points of the aspirin product with the known melting points of aspirin and salicylic acid.

Report Sheet

Date _____   Name _____

Section _____   Team _____

Instructor _____

Pre-Lab Study Questions

1. What are esters?

2. Why are buffers added to some aspirin products?

3. Old aspirin sometimes smells like vinegar. Why?

A. Carboxylic Acids and Their Salts

	Acetic Acid	**Benzoic Acid**
A.1 Condensed structural formulas		
A.2 Solubility in cold water		
A.3 pH		
A.4 Solubility in hot water		
A.5 Structure of salt		

Report Sheet

Questions and Problems

Q.1 How does NaOH affect the solubility of benzoic acid in water? Why?

Q.2 Write the names of the following carboxylic acids and esters:

a.
$$CH_3CH_2CH_2 - \overset{\overset{\displaystyle O}{\|}}{C} - OH$$

b.
$$CH_3CH_2\overset{\overset{\displaystyle O}{\|}}{C} - OCH_3$$

Q.3 Why are there differences in the solubility of the carboxylic acids in part A?

B. Esters

B.1 Equation for the formation of methyl acetate

Report Sheet

B.2 **Condensed Structural Formulas of Alcohol and Carboxylic Acid**	B.3 **Odor of Ester**	**Condensed Structural Formula and Name of Ester**
Methanol and salicylic acid		
1-Pentanol and acetic acid		
1-Octanol and acetic acid		
Benzyl alcohol and acetic acid		
1-Propanol and acetic acid		

Report Sheet

C. Preparation of Aspirin

C.1 Mass of flask _____

Mass of flask and salicylic acid _____

C.2 Mass of watch glass _____

Mass of watch glass and crude aspirin product _____

Calculations

C.3 Mass of salicyclic acid _____

C.4 Possible (maximum) yield of aspirin
(*Show calculations.*) _____

C.5 Mass of crude aspirin _____

C.6 Percent yield
(*Show calculations.*) _____

C.7 Melting point (°C) of aspirin product (optional) _____

Questions and Problems

Q.4 Write the structural formula for aspirin. Label the ester group and the carboxylic acid group.

Q.5 In the preparation of aspirin, water is added to the reaction flask. Why?

Q.6 If a typical aspirin tablet contains 325 mg aspirin (the rest is starch binder), how many tablets could you prepare from the aspirin you made in lab?

Carbohydrates

Goals

- Identify the characteristic functional groups of carbohydrates.
- Describe common carbohydrates and their sources.
- Observe physical and chemical properties of some common carbohydrates.
- Use physical and chemical tests to distinguish between monosaccharides, disaccharides, and polysaccharides.
- Relate the process of digestion to the hydrolysis of carbohydrates.

Discussion

Carbohydrates in our diet are our major source of energy. Foods high in carbohydrates include potatoes, bread, pasta, and rice. If we take in more carbohydrate than we need for energy, the excess is converted to fat, which can lead to a weight gain. The carbohydrate family is organized into three classes, which are the monosaccharides, disaccharides, and polysaccharides.

A. Monosaccharides

Monosaccharides contain C, H, and O in units of $(CH_2O)_n$. Most common monosaccharides have six carbon atoms (hexoses) with a general formula of $C_6H_{12}O_6$. They contain many hydroxyl groups (–OH) along with a carbonyl group. The aldoses are monosaccharides with an aldehyde group, and ketoses contain a ketone group.

Monosaccharides		Sources
Glucose	$C_6H_{12}O_6$	Fruit juices, honey, corn syrup
Galactose	$C_6H_{12}O_6$	Lactose hydrolysis
Fructose	$C_6H_{12}O_6$	Fruit juices, honey, sucrose hydrolysis

Glucose, a hexose, is the most common monosaccharide; it is also known as blood sugar.

D-Glucose

The letter D refers to the orientation of the hydroxyl group on the chiral carbon that is farthest from the carbonyl group at the top of the chain (carbon 1). The D- and L-isomers of glyceraldehyde illustrate the position of the –OH on the central, chiral atom.

From *Essential Laboratory Manual for Chemistry: An Introduction to General, Organic, and Biological Chemistry*, Ninth Edition, Karen C. Timberlake. Copyright © 2007 by Pearson Education, Inc. Published by Benjamin Cummings. All rights reserved.

D-Glyceraldehyde   L-Glyceraldehyde

Haworth Structures

Most of the time glucose exists in a ring structure, which forms when the OH on carbon 5 forms a hemiacetal bond with the aldehyde group. In the Haworth structure the new hydroxyl group on carbon 1 may be drawn above carbon 1 (the β form) or below carbon 1 (the α form).

D-Glucose α-D-Glucose β-D-Glucose

B. Disaccharides

The disaccharides contain two of the common monosaccharides. Some common disaccharides include maltose, sucrose (table sugar), and lactose (milk sugar).

Disaccharides	Sources	Monosaccharides
Maltose	Germinating grains, starch hydrolysis	Glucose + glucose
Lactose	Milk, yogurt, ice cream	Glucose + galactose
Sucrose	Sugar cane, sugar beets	Glucose + fructose

In a disaccharide, two monosaccharides form a glycosidic bond with the loss of water. For example, in maltose, two glucose units are linked by an α-1,4-glycosidic bond.

α-Maltose

C. Polysaccharides

Polysaccharides are long-chain polymers that contain many thousands of monosaccharides (usually glucose units) joined together by glycosidic bonds. Three important polysaccharides are starch, cellulose, and glycogen. They all contain glucose units, but differ in the type of glycosidic bonds and the amount of branching in the molecule.

Polysaccharides	Found in	Monosaccharides
Starch (amylose, amylopectin)	Rice, wheat, grains, cereals	Glucose
Glycogen	Muscle, liver	Glucose
Cellulose	Wood, plants, paper, cotton	Glucose

Starch is an insoluble storage form of glucose found in rice, wheat, potatoes, beans, and cereals. Starch is composed of two kinds of polysaccharides, amylose and amylopectin. *Amylose*, which makes up about 20% of starch, consists of α-D-glucose molecules connected by α-1,4-glycosidic bonds in a continuous chain. A typical polymer of amylose may contain from 250 to 4000 glucose units.

α-1,4-Glycosidic bonds in amylose

Amylopectin is a branched-chain polysaccharide that makes up as much as 80% of starch. In amylopectin, α-1,4-glycosidic bonds connect most of the glucose molecules. However, at about every 25 glucose units, there are branches of glucose molecules attached by α-1,6-glycosidic bonds between carbon 1 of the branch and carbon 6 in the main chain.

Amylopectin

Carbohydrates

Cellulose is the major structural material of wood and plants. Cotton is almost pure cellulose. In cellulose, glucose molecules form a long unbranched chain similar to amylose except that β-1,4-glycosidic bonds connect the glucose molecules. The β isomers are aligned in parallel rows that are held in place by hydrogen bonds between the rows. This gives a rigid structure for cell walls in wood and fiber and makes cellulose more resistant to hydrolysis.

D. Benedict's Test for Reducing Sugars

All of the monosaccharides and most of the disaccharides can be oxidized. When the cyclic structure opens, the aldehyde group is available for oxidation. Reagents such as Benedict's reagent contain Cu^{2+} ion that is reduced. Therefore, all the sugars that react with Benedict's reagent are called *reducing sugars*. Ketoses also act as reducing sugars because the ketone group on carbon 2 isomerizes to give an aldehyde group on carbon 1.

When oxidation of a sugar occurs, the Cu^{2+} is reduced to Cu^{+}, which forms a red precipitate of cuprous oxide, $Cu_2O(s)$. The color of the precipitate varies from green to gold to red depending on the concentration of the reducing sugar.

Sucrose is not a reducing sugar because it cannot revert to the open-chain form that would provide the aldehyde group needed to reduce the cupric ion.

Sucrose

E. Seliwanoff's Test for Ketoses

Seliwanoff's test is used to distinguish between hexoses with a ketone group and hexoses that are aldehydes. With ketoses, a deep red color is formed rapidly. Aldoses give a light pink color that takes a longer time to develop. The test is most sensitive for fructose, which is a ketose.

F. Fermentation Test

Most monosaccharides and disaccharides undergo fermentation in the presence of yeast. The products of fermentation are ethyl alcohol (CH_3CH_2OH) and carbon dioxide (CO_2). The formation of bubbles of carbon dioxide is used to confirm the fermentation process.

$$\underset{\text{Glucose}}{C_6H_{12}O_6} \overset{\text{yeast}}{\longrightarrow} \underset{\text{Ethanol}}{2C_2H_5OH} + 2CO_2(g)$$

Although enzymes are present for the hydrolysis of most disaccharides, they are not available for lactose. The enzymes needed for the fermentation of galactose are not present in yeast. Lactose and galactose give negative results with the fermentation test.

G. Iodine Test for Polysaccharides

When iodine (I_2) is added to amylose, the helical shape of the unbranched polysaccharide traps iodine molecules, producing a deep blue-black complex. Amylopectin, cellulose, and glycogen react with iodine to give red to brown colors. Glycogen produces a reddish-purple color. Monosaccharides and disaccharides are too small to trap iodine molecules and do not form dark colors with iodine.

H. Hydrolysis of Disaccharides and Polysaccharides

Disaccharides hydrolyze in the presence of an acid to give the individual monosaccharides.

$$\text{Sucrose} + H_2O \overset{H^+}{\longrightarrow} \text{Glucose} + \text{Fructose}$$

In the laboratory, we use water and acid to hydrolyze starches, which produce smaller saccharides such as maltose. Eventually, the hydrolysis reaction converts maltose to glucose molecules. In the body, enzymes in our saliva and from the pancreas carry out the hydrolysis. Complete hydrolysis produces glucose, which provides about 50% of our nutritional calories.

$$\text{Amylose, amylopectin} \overset{\substack{H^+ \text{ or} \\ \text{amylase}}}{\longrightarrow} \text{dextrins} \overset{\substack{H^+ \text{ or} \\ \text{amylase}}}{\longrightarrow} \text{maltose} \overset{\substack{H^+ \text{ or} \\ \text{maltase}}}{\longrightarrow} \text{many D-glucose units}$$

Lab Information

Time: 2–3 hr

Comments: Tear out the report sheets and place them next to the matching procedures.
In the study of carbohydrates, it is helpful to review stereoisomers and the formation of hemiacetals.

Related Topics: Carbohydrates, hemiacetals, stereoisomers, aldohexoses, ketohexoses, chiral compounds, Fischer projection, Haworth structures, reducing sugars, fermentation

Experimental Procedures

A. Monosaccharides

Materials: Organic model kits or prepared models

A.1 Make or observe models of L-glyceraldehyde and D-glyceraldehyde. Draw the Fischer projections.

A.2 Draw the Fischer projection for D-glucose. Draw the Haworth (cyclic) formulas for the α and β anomers.

A.3 Draw the Fischer projections for D-fructose and D-galactose. Draw the Haworth (cyclic) formulas for the α anomers of each.

B. Disaccharides

B.1 Using Haworth formulas, write the structure for α-D-maltose. Look at a model if available.

B.2 Write an equation for the hydrolysis of α-D-maltose by adding H_2O to the glycosidic bond.

B.3 Using Haworth formulas, write an equation for the formation of α-D-lactose from β-D-galactose and α-D-glucose.

B.4 Draw the structure of sucrose and circle the glycosidic bond.

C. Polysaccharides

C.1 Draw a portion of amylose using four units of α-D-glucose. Indicate the glycosidic bonds.

C.2 Describe how the structure of amylopectin differs from the structure of amylose.

C.3 Draw a portion of cellulose using four units of β-D-glucose. Indicate the glycosidic bonds.

D. Benedict's Test for Reducing Sugars

Materials: Test tubes, 400-mL beaker, droppers, hot plate or Bunsen burner, 5- or 10-mL graduated cylinder, Benedict's reagent, 2% carbohydrate solutions: glucose, fructose, sucrose, lactose, and starch

Place 10 drops of solutions of glucose, fructose, sucrose, lactose, starch, and water in separate test tubes. Label each test tube. Add 2 mL of Benedict's reagent to each sample. Place the test tubes in a boiling water bath for 3–4 minutes. The formation of a greenish to reddish-orange color indicates the presence of a reducing sugar. If the solution is the same color as the Benedict's reagent in water (the control), there has been no oxidation reaction. Record your observations. Classify each as a reducing or nonreducing sugar.

E. Seliwanoff's Test for Ketoses

Materials: Test tubes, 400-mL beaker, droppers, hot plate or Bunsen burner, 5- or 10-mL graduated cylinder, Seliwanoff's reagent, 2% carbohydrate solutions: glucose, fructose, sucrose, lactose, and starch

Place 10 drops of solutions of glucose, fructose, sucrose, lactose, and starch, and water in separate test tubes. Add 2 mL of Seliwanoff's reagent to each. ***The reagent contains concentrated HCl. Use carefully.***

Place the test tubes in a boiling hot water bath and note the time. After 1 minute, observe the colors in the test tubes. A rapid formation of a deep red color indicates the presence of a ketose. Record your results as a fast color change, slow change, or no change.

F. Fermentation Test

Materials: Fermentation tubes (or small and large test tubes), baker's yeast, 2% carbohydrate solutions: glucose, fructose, sucrose, lactose, and starch

Fill fermentation tubes with a solution of glucose, fructose, sucrose, lactose, starch, and water. Add 0.2 g of yeast to each and mix well. See Figure 1.

Figure 1 Fermentation tube filled with a carbohydrate solution

If fermentation tubes are not available, use small test tubes placed upside down in larger test tubes. Cover the mouth of the large test tube with filter paper or cardboard. Place your hand firmly over the paper cover and invert. When the small test tube inside has completely filled with the mixture, return the larger test tube to an upright position. See Figure 2.

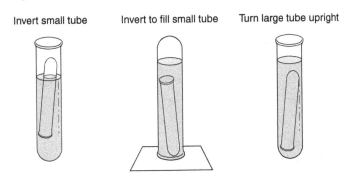

Figure 2 Test tubes used as fermentation tubes

Set the tubes aside. At the end of the laboratory period, and again at the next laboratory period, look for gas bubbles in the fermentation tubes or inside the small tubes. Record your observations. See Figure 3.

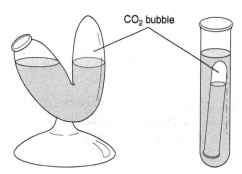

CO₂ bubble

Figure 3   Fermentation tubes with CO_2 bubbles

G.   Iodine Test for Polysaccharides

Materials: Spot plate or test tubes, droppers, iodine reagent, 2% carbohydrate solutions in dropper bottles: glucose, fructose, sucrose, lactose, and starch

Using a spot plate, place 5 drops of each carbohydrate solution (glucose, fructose, sucrose, lactose, starch) and water in the wells. (If you do not have a spot plate, use small test tubes.) Add 1 drop of iodine solution to each sample. A dark blue-black color is a positive test for amylose in starch. A red or brown color indicates the presence of other polysaccharides. Record your results.

H.   Hydrolysis of Disaccharides and Polysaccharides

Materials: Test tubes, 10-mL graduated cylinder, 400-mL beaker (boiling water bath), hot plate or Bunsen burner, spot plate or watch glass, 10% HCl, 10% NaOH, red litmus paper, iodine reagent, Benedict's reagent, 2% starch and sucrose solutions in dropper bottles.

Place 3 mL of 2% starch in two test tubes and 3 mL of 2% sucrose solution in two more test tubes. To one sample each of sucrose and starch, add 20 drops of 10% HCl. To the other samples of sucrose and starch, add 20 drops of H_2O. Label the test tubes and heat in a boiling water bath for 10 minutes.

Remove the test tubes from the water bath and let them cool. To the samples containing HCl, add 10% NaOH (about 20 drops) until one drop of the mixture turns litmus paper blue, indicating the HCl has been neutralized. Test the samples for hydrolysis as follows:

> **Iodine Test**   Place 5 drops of each solution on a spot plate or watch glass. Add 1 drop of iodine reagent to each. Record observations. Determine if hydrolysis has occurred in each.

> **Benedict's Test**   Add 2 mL of Benedict's reagent to each of the samples and heat in a boiling water bath for 3–4 minutes. Determine if hydrolysis has occurred in each.

Report Sheet

Date _____   Name _____

Section _____   Team _____

Instructor _____

Pre-Lab Study Questions

1. What are some sources of carbohydrates in your diet?

2. What does the D in D-glucose mean?

3. What is the bond that links monosaccharides in di- and polysaccharides?

4. How can the iodine test be used to distinguish between amylose and glycogen?

A. Monosaccharides

A.1 Fischer projections

L-glyceraldehyde   D-glyceraldehyde

How does the L-glyceraldehyde differ from the D-glyceraldehyde?

Report Sheet

A.2 Fischer projection of D-glucose

Haworth (cyclic) formulas

α-D-glucose

β-D-glucose

A.3 Fischer projection of D-fructose

Haworth (cyclic) formula for α-D-fructose

Fischer projection of D-galactose

Haworth (cyclic) formula for α-D-galactose

Questions and Problems

Q.1 How does the structure of D-glucose compare to the structure of D-galactose?

Report Sheet

B. Disaccharides

B.1   Structure of α-D-maltose

B.2   Equation for the hydrolysis of α-D-maltose

B.3   Formation of α-D-lactose

B.4   Structure of sucrose

Questions and Problems

Q.2   What is the type of glycosidic bond in maltose?

Q.3   Why does maltose have both α and β anomers? Explain.

Report Sheet

C. Polysaccharides

C.1 A portion of amylose

C.2 Comparison of amylopectin to amylose

C.3 A portion of cellulose

Questions and Problems

Q.4 What is the monosaccharide that results from the complete hydrolysis of amylose?

Q.5 What is the difference in the structure of amylose and cellulose?

Report Sheet

Results of Carbohydrate Tests

	D. Benedict's Test	E. Seliwanoff's Test	F. Fermentation Test	G. Iodine Test
Glucose				
Fructose				
Sucrose				
Lactose				
Starch				
Water				

Questions and Problems

Q.6 From the results above, list the sugars that are reducing sugars and those that are not.

Reducing sugars

Nonreducing sugars

Q.7 What sugars are ketoses?

Q.8 What sugars give a positive fermentation test?

Q.9 Which carbohydrates give a blue-black color in the iodine test?

Report Sheet

Q.10 What carbohydrate(s) would have the following test results?

    a. Produces a reddish-orange solid with Benedict's and a red color with Seliwanoff's reagent in 1 minute

    b. Gives a color change with Benedict's test, a light orange color with Seliwanoff's reagent after 5 minutes, and produces no bubbles during fermentation

    c. Gives no color change with Benedict's or Seliwanoff's test, but turns a blue-black color with iodine reagent

H.   Hydrolysis of Disaccharides and Polysaccharides

Results	Sucrose + H_2O	Sucrose + HCl	Starch + H_2O	Starch + HCl
Iodine test				
Benedict's test				
Hydrolysis products present				

Questions and Problems

Q.11 How do the results of the Benedict's test indicate that hydrolysis of sucrose and starch occurred?

Q.12 How do the results of the iodine test indicate that hydrolysis of starch occurred?

Lipids

Goals

- Observe the physical and chemical properties of some common lipids.
- Draw the structure of a typical triacylglycerol.
- Distinguish between saturated and unsaturated fats.
- Determine the degree of unsaturation of some fats.
- Prepare a hand lotion and determine the function of its components.

Discussion

A. Triacylglycerols

The triacylglycerols, commonly called fats or oils, are esters of glycerol and fatty acids. Fatty acids are long-chain carboxylic acids, usually 14 to 18 carbons in length. When the fatty acid contains double bonds, the triacylglycerol is referred to as an unsaturated fat. When the fatty acid consists of an alkane-like carbon chain, the triacylglycerol is a saturated fat. Table 1 gives the formulas of the common fatty acids and their melting points. At room temperature, saturated fats are usually solid and unsaturated fats are usually liquid.

Table 1 *Formulas, Melting Points, and Sources of Some Fatty Acids*

Carbon Atoms	Structural Formula	Melting Point (°C)	Common Name	Source
Saturated fatty acids (single carbon–carbon bonds)				
12	$CH_3(CH_2)_{10}COOH$	44	lauric	coconut
14	$CH_3(CH_2)_{12}COOH$	54	myristic	nutmeg
16	$CH_3(CH_2)_{14}COOH$	63	palmitic	palm
18	$CH_3(CH_2)_{16}COOH$	70	stearic	animal fat
Monounsaturated fatty acids (one cis double bond)				
16	$CH_3(CH_2)_5CH{=}CH(CH_2)_7COOH$	1	palmitoleic	butter fat
18	$CH_3 (CH_2)_7CH{=}CH(CH_2)_7COOH$	4	oleic	olives, corn
Polyunsaturated fatty acids (two or more cis double bonds)				
18	$CH_3(CH_2)_4CH{=}CHCH_2CH{=}CH(CH_2)_7COOH$	−5	linoleic	safflower, sunflower
18	$CH_3CH_2CH{=}CHCH_2CH{=}CHCH_2CH{=}CH(CH_2)_7COOH$	−11	linolenic	corn

From *Essential Laboratory Manual for Chemistry: An Introduction to General, Organic, and Biological Chemistry*, Ninth Edition, Karen C. Timberlake. Copyright © 2007 by Pearson Education, Inc. Published by Benjamin Cummings. All rights reserved.

Lipids

Fats that contain mostly saturated fatty acids have a higher melting point than fats with more unsaturated fatty acids.

$$
\begin{array}{ccc}
\text{CH}_2\text{—OH} & \text{HO—}\overset{\overset{\textstyle O}{\|}}{\text{C}}(\text{CH}_2)_{14}\text{CH}_3 & \text{CH}_2\text{—O—}\overset{\overset{\textstyle O}{\|}}{\text{C}}(\text{CH}_2)_{14}\text{CH}_3 \\
| & \overset{\overset{\textstyle O}{\|}}{} & | \quad\quad \overset{\overset{\textstyle O}{\|}}{} \\
\text{CH—OH} \;+\; & \text{HO—}\text{C}(\text{CH}_2)_{14}\text{CH}_3 \;\longrightarrow\; & \text{CH—O—}\text{C}(\text{CH}_2)_{14}\text{CH}_3 \;+\; 3\ \text{H}_2\text{O} \\
| & \overset{\overset{\textstyle O}{\|}}{} & | \quad\quad \overset{\overset{\textstyle O}{\|}}{} \\
\text{CH}_2\text{—OH} & \text{HO—}\text{C}(\text{CH}_2)_{14}\text{CH}_3 & \text{CH}_2\text{—O—}\text{C}(\text{CH}_2)_{14}\text{CH}_3
\end{array}
$$

Glycerol   3 Palmitic acids   Glyceryl palmitate (tripalmitin)

B. Physical Properties of Some Lipids and Fatty Acids

Lipids are a family of compounds that are grouped by similarities in solubility rather than structure. As a group, lipids are more soluble in nonpolar solvents such as ether, chloroform, or benzene. Most are not soluble in water. Important types of lipids include fats and oils, glycerophospholipids, and steroids. Compounds classified as lipids include fat-soluble vitamins A, D, E, and K; cholesterol; hormones; portions of cell membranes; and vegetable oils. Table 2 lists the classes of lipids.

Table 2 *Classes of Lipid Molecules*

Lipids	Components
Waxes	Fatty acid and long-chain alcohol
Fats and oils (triacylglycerols)	Fatty acids and glycerol
Glycerophospholipids	Fatty acids, glycerol, phosphate, amino alcohol
Steroids	A fused structure of three cyclohexanes and a cyclopentane

The structural formulas of three typical lipids are shown below:

$$\text{CH}_3\text{—(CH}_2)_{14}\text{—}\overset{\overset{\textstyle O}{\|}}{\text{C}}\text{—O—(CH}_2)_{29}\text{—CH}_3$$

Wax

$$
\begin{array}{l}
\text{CH}_2\text{—O—}\overset{\overset{\textstyle O}{\|}}{\text{C}}\text{—(CH}_2)_{16}\text{—CH}_3 \\
| \qquad\qquad \overset{\overset{\textstyle O}{\|}}{} \\
\text{CH—O—}\text{C}\text{—(CH}_2)_{16}\text{—CH}_3 \\
| \qquad\qquad \overset{\overset{\textstyle O}{\|}}{} \\
\text{CH}_2\text{—O—}\text{C}\text{—(CH}_2)_{16}\text{—CH}_3
\end{array}
$$

Triacylglycerol, a fat

Cholesterol, a steroid

C. Bromine Test for Unsaturation

The presence of unsaturation in a fatty acid or a triacylglycerol can be detected by the bromine test, which you used in an earlier experiment to detect double bonds in alkenes. If the orange color of the bromine solution fades quickly, an addition reaction has occurred and the oil or fat is unsaturated.

Bromine adds to the double bond

$$CH_2-O-\overset{\overset{\displaystyle O}{\|}}{C}(CH_2)_7CH=CH(CH_2)_7CH_3$$

$$CH-O-\overset{\overset{\displaystyle O}{\|}}{C}(CH_2)_{16}CH_3 \quad + Br_2 \longrightarrow$$

$$CH_2-O-\overset{\overset{\displaystyle O}{\|}}{C}(CH_2)_{16}CH_3$$

$$CH_2-O-\overset{\overset{\displaystyle O}{\|}}{C}(CH_2)_7\overset{\overset{\displaystyle Br}{|}}{CH}-\overset{\overset{\displaystyle Br}{|}}{CH}(CH_2)_7CH_3$$

$$CH-O-\overset{\overset{\displaystyle O}{\|}}{C}(CH_2)_{16}CH_3$$

$$CH_2-O-\overset{\overset{\displaystyle O}{\|}}{C}(CH_2)_{16}CH_3$$

D. Preparation of Hand Lotion

We use hand lotions and creams to soften our skin and reduce dryness. Typically, the formulation of a hand lotion consists of several components such as stearic acid, lanolin, triethanolamine, cetyl alcohol, glycerin (glycerol), water, and usually a fragrance. Lanolin from wool consists of a mixture of waxes.

Cetyl alcohol $\quad\quad CH_3(CH_2)_{15}OH$

Stearic acid $\quad\quad CH_3-(CH_2)_{16}-\overset{\overset{\displaystyle O}{\|}}{C}-OH$

Glycerol (glycerine)
$$CH_2-OH$$
$$|$$
$$CH-OH$$
$$|$$
$$CH_2-OH$$

Triethanolamine
$$CH_2CH_2OH$$
$$|$$
$$HOCH_2CH_2-N-CH_2CH_2OH$$

Because lipids are nonpolar, they protect and soften by preventing the loss of moisture from the skin. Some of the components help emulsify the polar and nonpolar ingredients. In this experiment, we will see how the physical and chemical properties of lipids are used to prepare a hand lotion.

Lab Information

Time: 3 hr

Comments: Bromine can cause severe chemical burns. Use carefully.
                   Tear out the Lab report sheets and place them beside the matching procedures.

Related topics: Fatty acids, saturated and unsaturated fatty acids, lipids, triglycerides.

Experimental Procedures

BE SURE YOU ARE WEARING YOUR SAFETY GOGGLES!

A.   Triacylglycerols

Materials: Organic model kits or models

A.1   Use an organic model kit or observe prepared models of a molecule of glycerol and three molecules of ethanoic acid. What are the functional groups on each? Draw their structures.

A.2   Form ester bonds between the hydroxy groups on glycerol and the carboxylic acid groups of the ethanoic acid molecules. In the process, three molecules of water are removed. Write an equation for the formation of the glyceryl ethanoate.

Carry out the reverse process, which is hydrolysis. Add the components of water to break the ester bond. Add an arrow to the equation to show the reverse direction for the hydrolysis reaction.

B.   Physical Properties of Some Lipids and Fatty Acids

Materials: Test tubes and stoppers, dropper bottles or solids: stearic acid, oleic acid, olive oil, safflower oil, lecithin, cholesterol, vitamin A capsules, spatulas, CH_2Cl_2 (optional)

To seven separate test tubes, add 5 drops or the amount of solid lipid held on the tip of a spatula: stearic acid, oleic acid, olive oil, safflower oil, lecithin, cholesterol, vitamin A (puncture a capsule or use cod liver oil).

Appearance and Odor

B.1   Classify each as a triacylglycerol (fat or oil), fatty acid, steroid, or phospholipid.

B.2   Describe their appearance.

B.3   Describe their odors.

Solubility in a Polar Solvent *(May be a demonstration)*

B.4   Add about 2 mL of water to each of the test tubes. Stopper and shake each test tube. Record your observations.

Solubility in a Nonpolar Solvent *(Optional or demonstration)*

B.5   Place 5 drops, or a small amount of solid, of the following in separate test tubes: stearic acid, oleic oil, olive oil, safflower oil, lecithin, cholesterol, and vitamin A. Add 1 mL (20 drops) methylene chloride, CH_2Cl_2, to each sample. Record the solubility of the lipids. *Save the test tubes and samples of stearic acid oleic acid, olive oil and safflower oil for part C.*

C. Bromine Test for Unsaturation

Materials: Samples from B.5, 1% Br_2 in methylene chloride

To the samples from B.5, add 1% bromine solution drop by drop until a permanent red-orange color is obtained or until 20 drops have been added.

Caution: Avoid contact with bromine solution; it can cause painful burns. Do not breathe the fumes.

Record your observations. Determine if the red-orange color fades rapidly or persists.

D. Preparation of Hand Lotion

Materials: Stearic acid, cetyl alcohol, lanolin (anhydrous), triethanolamine, glycerol, ethanol, distilled water, fragrance (optional), commercial hand lotions, 10-mL graduated cylinder, 50-mL graduated cylinder, 50-mL or 100-mL beakers, thermometer, 100-mL beakers, 250-mL beaker for water bath, Bunsen burner, iron ring, wire screen, stirring rods, tongs, pH paper

Team project: D.1, D.2, and D.3 may be prepared by different teams in the lab.

D.1 Obtain the following substances and combine in two 50-mL or 100-mL beakers. Use a laboratory balance to weigh out the solid substances. Use a 10-mL graduated cylinder to measure small volumes, and a 50-mL graduated cylinder to measure larger volumes.

Beaker 1		**Beaker 2**	
Stearic acid	3 g	Glycerin	2 mL
Cetyl alcohol	1 g	Water	50 mL
Lanolin (anhydrous)	2 g		
Triethanolamine	1 mL		

Water bath: Fill a 250-mL beaker about 2/3 full of water. Place the beaker on an iron ring covered with a wire screen. Lower a second iron ring that fits around the 250-mL beaker to stabilize it. Turn on the Bunsen burner to heat the water.

Using a pair of crucible tongs, hold Beaker 1 (four ingredients) in the water bath and heat to 80°C or until all the compounds have melted. Remove.

Using a pair of crucible tongs, place Beaker 2 (two ingredients) in the same water bath and heat to 80°C.

While still warm, slowly pour the glycerol-water mixture from Beaker 2 into Beaker 1 (four ingredients) as you stir. Add 5.0 mL of ethanol and a few drops of fragrance, if desired. Continue to stir for 3–5 minutes until a smooth, creamy lotion is obtained. If the resulting product is too thick, add more warm water.

Describe the smoothness and appearance of the hand lotion.

D.2 Repeat the experiment, but omit the triethanolamine from Beaker 1. Compare the properties of the resulting hand lotion to the one obtained in D.1 and to commercial hand lotions.

D.3 Repeat the experiment, but omit the stearic acid from Beaker 1. Compare the properties and textures of the resulting hand lotion to the one obtained in D.1 and to commercial hand lotions.

D.4 Determine the pH of the hand lotions you and others in your lab have prepared along with any commercial hand lotions.

Report Sheet

Date _____   Name _____

Section _____   Team _____

Instructor _____

Pre-Lab Study Questions

1. What is the functional group in a triacylglycerol?

2. Write the structure of linolenic acid. Why is it an unsaturated fatty acid?

A.   Triacylglycerols

A.1   Structure of glycerol   Structure of ethanoic acid

A.2   Reversible equation for the esterification and hydrolysis of glyceryl ethanoate

Report Sheet

B. Physical Properties of Some Lipids and Fatty Acids

Lipid	B.1 Type of Lipid	B.2 Appearance	B.3 Odor	B.4 Soluble in Water?	B.5 Soluble in CH_2Cl_2?
Stearic acid					
Oleic acid					
Olive oil					
Safflower oil					
Lecithin					
Cholesterol					
Vitamin A					

Questions and Problems

Q.1 Why are the compounds in part B classified as lipids?

Q.2 What type of solvent is needed to remove an oil spot? Why?

Report Sheet

C. Bromine Test for Unsaturation

Compound	Drops of Bromine Solution	Saturated or Unsaturated?
Fatty acids		
Stearic acid		
Oleic acid		
Triacylglycerols		
Safflower oil		
Olive oil		

Questions and Problems

Q.3 a. Write the condensed structural formulas of stearic acid and oleic acid.

Stearic acid

Oleic acid

b. Which fatty acid is unsaturated?

c. The melting point of stearic acid is 70°C, and that of oleic acid is 4°C. Explain the difference.

d. From the results of experiment C, how can you tell which is more unsaturated, oleic acid or stearic acid?

Report Sheet

D. Preparation of Hand Lotion

Descriptions of the hand lotions		
D.1	D.2 (without triethanolamine)	D.3 (without stearic acid)
D.4 pH of the hand lotions		
pH of commercial hand lotions		
Brand_____	Brand_____	Brand_____
pH _____	pH _____	pH _____

Questions and Problems

Q.4   How does omitting triethanolamine affect the properties and appearance of the hand lotion?

Q.5   How does omitting stearic acid affect the properties and appearance of the hand lotion?

Q.6   What would be a reason to have triethaonolamine and stearic acid as ingredients in hand lotion?

Peptides and Proteins

Goals

- Identify the structural patterns of proteins.
- Observe the denaturation of proteins.
- Use the isoelectric point of casein in milk to isolate the protein.
- Use chemical tests to identify proteins and amino acids.

Discussion

A. Peptide Bonds

A dipeptide forms when two amino acids bond together. A peptide (or amide) bond forms between the carboxylic acid of one amino acid and the amino group of the next amino acid with the loss of H_2O.

Amino acid (1)   Amino acid (2)   Dipeptide

In the reverse reaction, hydrolysis, water adds to the peptide bond to yield the individual amino acids. For example, the dipeptide glycylalanine hydrolyzes to give the amino acids glycine and alanine.

Glycylalanine (Gly-Ala), a dipeptide   Glycine   Alanine

B. Structure of Proteins

When many amino acids are joined by peptide bonds they make a polypeptide. If more than 50 amino acids are in the peptide chain, it is usually considered to be a protein. Proteins make up many important features in the body including skin, muscle, cartilage, hair, fingernails, enzymes, and hormones. Proteins have specific structures, which are determined by the sequence of the amino acids. The peptide bonds that join one amino acid to the next are the *primary* level of protein structure. *Secondary* structures include the alpha (α) helix formed by the coiling of the peptide chain, or a β-pleated sheet structure formed between protein strands.

The secondary structures are held in place by many hydrogen bonds between the oxygen atoms of the carbonyl groups and the hydrogen atoms of the amide group. At the *tertiary* level, interactions between the side groups such as ionic bonds or salt bridges, disulfide bonds, and hydrophilic bonds give the protein a compact shape. Such tertiary structures are evident in the spherical shape of globular proteins. Similar interactions between two or more tertiary units produce the *quaternary* structure of many active proteins.

From *Essential Laboratory Manual for Chemistry: An Introduction to General, Organic, and Biological Chemistry*, Ninth Edition, Karen C. Timberlake. Copyright © 2007 by Pearson Education, Inc. Published by Benjamin Cummings. All rights reserved.

C.   Denaturation of Proteins

Denaturation of a protein occurs when certain conditions or agents disrupt the bonds that hold together the secondary or tertiary structures of a protein. Proteins are denatured with heat, acid, base, ethanol, tannic acid, and heavy metal ions (silver, lead, and mercury). In most cases, the protein coagulates. Heat increases the motion of the atoms and disrupts the hydrogen bonds and the hydrophobic (nonpolar) attractions. Strong acids and bases disrupt the ionic bonds between amino acids with acidic and basic side groups. Alcohol, an organic solvent, destroys hydrogen bonds. The heavy metal ions, Ag^+, Pb^{2+}, and Hg^{2+}, react with the sulfur groups and carboxylic acid groups, which prevents the formation of the cross-links for tertiary structures and quaternary structures.

D.   Isolation of Casein (Milk Protein)

A typical source of protein is milk, which contains the protein casein. When the pH of a sample of non-fat milk is acidified, it reaches its isoelectric point, and the protein separates out of the solution. The change in pH disrupts the bonds that hold the tertiary structure together. Adjusting the pH of the mixture causes the casein to solidify so it can be removed. A similar process is used in the making of yogurt, cheeses, and cottage cheese. An enzyme provides the acid for the denaturation of the protein for those products. In this experiment, the mass of a quantity of milk and the mass of isolated casein will be determined. From this data, the percent casein in milk will be calculated.

E.   Color Tests for Proteins

Certain tests give color products with amino acids, peptides, and/or proteins. The results of the test can be used to detect certain groups or type of bonds within proteins or amino acids.

Biuret test The biuret test is positive for a peptide or protein with two or more peptide bonds. In the *biuret test*, the blue color of a basic solution of Cu^{2+} turns to a violet color when a tripeptide or larger peptide is present. Individual amino acids and dipeptides do not react with the reagent, and the solution will remain blue (negative).

Ninhydrin test The ninhydrin test is used to detect amino acids and most proteins. In the test, most amino acids produce a blue-violet color. Proline and hydroxyproline give a yellow color.

Xanthoproteic test This test is specific for amino acids that contain an aromatic ring. Concentrated nitric acid reacts with the side chains of tyrosine and tryptophan to give nitro-substituted benzene rings that appear as yellow-colored products.

Lab Information

Time: 2–3 hr

Comments: In protein color tests, be sure to note the color of the reagent before you add it to the samples.
Concentrated HNO_3 and 10% NaOH are extremely corrosive and damage skin and eyes. Tear out the report sheets and place them beside the matching procedures.

Related topics: Amino acids, peptide bonds, structural levels of proteins, denaturation of proteins

Experimental Procedures

GOGGLES REQUIRED!

A. Peptide Bonds

Materials: Organic model set

A.1 Make models of glycine and serine. Remove the components of water (H—OH) from an amino and carboxylic acid group to form the dipeptides glycylserine and serylglycine. Draw each of their structures.

A.2 Demonstrate hydrolysis of the dipeptide serylglycine by breaking the peptide bond and adding the components of H_2O. Write a balanced equation for the hydrolysis.

B. Structure of Proteins

Materials: Organic model set

B.1 Make a model of an amino acid. Draw its structure and name it. Share your model with two other students, or groups of students who will make models of other amino acids. Line the models up and write their amino acid structures.

B.2 Form peptide bonds between the amino acids by removing the components of water. Write an equation for the formation of a tripeptide. Use the symbols for the amino acids to write the tripeptide order. Rearrange the amino acids and prepare a different tripeptide. Write the structure and name of the new tripeptide.

C. Denaturation of Proteins

Materials: Test tubes, test tube holder, 10-mL graduated cylinder, 1% egg albumin (or an egg, cheesecloth, and beaker), 10% HNO_3, 10% NaOH, 95% ethyl alcohol, 1% $AgNO_3$ (dropper bottle)

A fresh egg albumin solution can be prepared by mixing the white from one egg with 200 mL of water and filtering the mixture through cheesecloth into a beaker.

Place 2–3 mL of egg albumin solution in each of five test tubes. Use one sample for each of the following tests. Record your observations and give a brief explanation for the results.

C.1 **Heat** Using a test tube holder, heat the egg albumin solution over a low flame. Describe any changes in the solution.

C.2 **Acid** Add 2 mL of 10% HNO_3.

C.3 **Base** Add 2 mL of 10% NaOH.

C.4 **Alcohol** Add 4 mL of 95% ethyl alcohol. Mix.

C.5 **Heavy metal ions** Add 10 drops of 1% $AgNO_3$.

D. Isolation of Casein (Milk Protein)

Materials: 150-mL beaker, hot plate or Bunsen burner, thermometer, funnel or Büchner filtration apparatus, filter paper, watch glass, nonfat milk, 10% acetic acid, dropper, pH paper, stirring rod

D.1 Weigh a 150-mL beaker. Add about 20 mL of nonfat milk to the beaker and weigh. Calculate the mass of the nonfat milk sample.

D.2 Using pH indicator paper, determine the pH of the milk sample.

D.3 Warm the sample on a hot plate or a Bunsen burner until the temperature reaches about 50°C. Remove the beaker and milk from the heat and add 10% acetic acid, drop by drop. You may need 2–3 mL. Stir continuously. At the isoelectric point, the casein (milk protein) becomes insoluble. When no further precipitation occurs, stop adding acid. If the liquid layer is not clear, heat the mixture gently for a few more minutes. Determine the pH at which the casein becomes insoluble in solution. This is the pH of the isoelectric point of casein.

D.4 Collect the solid protein using a funnel and filter paper or the Büchner filtration apparatus. Wash the protein with two 10-mL portions of water. Weigh a watch glass. Transfer the protein to the watch glass and let the protein dry. Weigh. Calculate the mass of milk protein. *Save for part E.*

D.5 Calculate the percentage of casein in the nonfat milk.

$$\% \text{ Casein} = \frac{\text{mass (g) of casein}}{\text{mass (g) of milk}} \times 100\%$$

E. Color Tests for Proteins

Materials: Test tubes, test tube rack, 10-mL graduated cylinder, boiling water bath, cold water bath, pH paper, spatula, dropper bottles of 1% amino acid solution (glycine, tyrosine), dropper bottles of 1% solutions of proteins (gelatin, egg albumin), casein from part D, 0.2% ninhydrin solution, concentrated HNO_3 (dropper bottle), 10% NaOH, 5% $CuSO_4$ (biuret), red litmus paper

E.1 **Biuret test** In four separate test tubes, place 2 mL of solutions of glycine, tyrosine, gelatin, and egg albumin. To the fifth tube, add a small amount of the solid casein (from part D), the amount held on the tip of a spatula. To each sample, add 2 mL of 10% NaOH and stir. Then add 5 drops of biuret reagent (5% $CuSO_4$), and stir. Record the color of each sample. The formation of a pink-violet color indicates the presence of a protein with two or more peptide bonds. If such a protein is not present, the blue color of the cupric sulfate will remain (negative result). Record the results and your conclusions.

E.2 **Ninhydrin test** In four separate test tubes, place 2 mL of the solutions of glycine, tyrosine, gelatin, and egg albumin. To the fifth tube, add a small amount of the solid casein (from part D), the amount held on the tip of a spatula. Add 1 mL of 0.2% ninhydrin solution to each sample. Place the test tubes in a boiling water bath for 4–5 minutes. Look for the formation of a blue-violet color. Record your observations.

E.3 **Xanthoproteic test** (*optional*) Place 1 mL of the solutions of glycine, tyrosine, gelatin, and egg albumin in four test tubes. To a fifth tube, add a small amount of casein (from part D). ***Cautiously*** add 10 drops of concentrated HNO_3 to each sample. Place the test tubes in a boiling water bath and heat for 3–4 minutes. Remove the test tubes, place them in cold water, and let them cool. Carefully add 10% NaOH, drop by drop, until the solution is just basic (turns red litmus blue). This may required 2–3 mL of NaOH. ***Caution: heat will be evolved.*** Look for the formation of a yellow-orange color, which may vary in intensity. Record your observations.

Report Sheet

Date _____   Name _____

Section _____   Team _____

Instructor _____

Pre-Lab Study Questions

1. What is a peptide bond?

2. How does the primary structure of proteins differ from the secondary structure?

A. Peptide Bonds

A.1   Structure of glycylserine

Structure of serylglycine

A.2   Hydrolysis of serylglycine

Report Sheet

B. Structure of Proteins

B.1 Amino acid structures and names

B.2 Equation for the formation of the first tripeptide

Order of amino acids using symbols

Equation for the formation of the second tripeptide

Order of amino acids using symbols

Report Sheet

C. Denaturation of Proteins

Treatment	Observations of Egg Albumin	Explanation
C.1 Heat		
C.2 Acid		
C.3 Base		
C.4 Alcohol		
C.5 Heavy metal ions		

Questions and Problems

Q.1 Why are heat and alcohol used to disinfect medical equipment?

Q.2 Why is milk given to someone who accidentally ingests a heavy metal ion such as silver or mercury?

Report Sheet

D. Isolation of Casein (Milk Protein)

D.1 Mass of beaker	
Mass of beaker and milk	
Mass of milk	
D.2 pH of milk	
D.3 pH when casein precipitates	
D.4 Mass of watch glass	
Mass of watch glass and casein	
Mass of casein	
D.5 Percent casein *Show calculations.*	

Questions and Problems

Q.3   Compare the pH of the milk sample and the pH at which the casein solid forms.

Q.4   How does a change in pH affect the structural levels of a protein?

Report Sheet

E.   Color Tests for Proteins

Observations of Color Tests			
Sample	E.1 **Biuret**	E.2 **Ninhydrin**	E.3 **Xanthoproteic**
Glycine			
Tyrosine			
Gelatin			
Egg albumin			
Casein (milk protein)			

Questions and Problems

Q.5   After working with HNO_3, a student noticed that she had a yellow spot on her hand. What might be the reason?

Q.6   Which samples give a negative biuret test? Why?

Q.7   What functional group gives a positive test in the xanthoproteic test?

Q.8   What tests could you use to determine whether an unlabeled test tube contained an amino acid or a protein?

DNA Components and Extraction

Goals

- Identify the components in DNA: purines, adenine and guanine, phosphate, and deoxyribose.
- Identify the monomer units in DNA.
- Extract and compare DNA samples from a variety of plant and animal cells.

Discussion

In the cells of all living things are molecules called nucleic acids that provide the information for cellular replication and growth by directing protein synthesis. There are two main types of nucleic acids: DNA (deoxyribonucleic acid), which carries the genetic code to each new generation of cells, and RNA (ribonucleic acid), which carries the instructions for a protein to the ribosomes where proteins are synthesized.

Every living organism contains DNA that provides the directions to make the proteins for the characteristics of that organism. The DNA in an onion has a set of directions to make an onion, whereas the DNA in a banana directs the growth of a banana. Each daughter cell is just like the parent cell because the DNA is duplicated in every cell division.

A. Components of DNA

Nucleic acids are polymers of repeating units known as nucleotides. There are millions of nucleotides in a single DNA molecule. RNA molecules are smaller and contain several thousand nucleotides. A nucleotide of DNA consists of a 5-carbon deoxyribose sugar, one of four nitrogenous bases, and a phosphate group. (See Figure 1.)

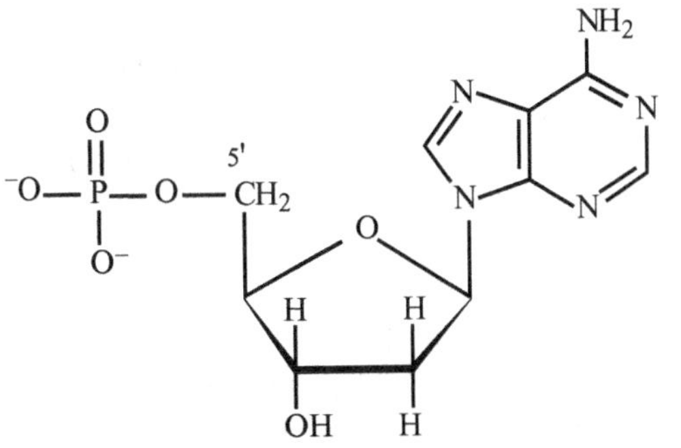

Deoxyadenosine 5'–monophosphate (dAMP)

Figure 1 One of four nucleotides found in DNA

From *Essential Laboratory Manual for Chemistry: An Introduction to General, Organic, and Biological Chemistry*, Ninth Edition, Karen C. Timberlake. Copyright © 2007 by Pearson Education, Inc. Published by Benjamin Cummings. All rights reserved.

In DNA, two bases are the purines adenine (A) and guanine (G) and the other two bases are the pyrimidines cytosine (C) and thymine (T). The nucleotides in RNA differ slightly; the sugar is ribose, and the pyrimidine uracil replaces thymine.

Pyrimidines			Purines	
Cytosine (C) (DNA and RNA)	Thymine (T) (DNA) only	Uracil (U) (RNA only)	Adenine (A) (DNA and RNA)	Guanine (G) (DNA and RNA)

B.   Extraction of DNA

In plant cells, DNA strands are combined with protein and RNA molecules. The extraction and isolation of DNA from a cell requires three processes (1) breaking down the cellular membranes, (2) heating the mixture and denaturing the proteins, and (3) precipitating the DNA as a white, stringy, fibrous material.

Step 1: Breaking down cell membranes

The plant or animal material containing the DNA is mixed with an extraction buffer and homogenized to break down the cell membranes. The extraction buffer consists of sodium dodecyl sulfate (SDS), ethylenediamine tetraacetic acid (EDTA), sodium chloride (NaCl), and sodium citrate. SDS disrupts the polar attractions that hold the cell membrane together. EDTA, a chelating agent, removes Mg^{2+} and Ca^{2+} ions that are needed by nucleases that degrade DNA. The NaCl binds with the negatively charged phosphate groups in the DNA fragments, which will cause them to precipitate out of an ethanol solution in step 3. The buffer and the following heat treatment cause lipids and proteins to precipitate out of solution.

Step 2: Heating and denaturing proteins

Heating denatures proteins and inactivates the nuclease enzymes that degrade DNA. If the nucleases remain active, they would hydrolyze DNA into its nucleotide components. When we cook, we heat foods to denature the protein. In addition, some people add a meat tenderizer, which contains a protease, to break down proteins further and make them more digestible.

Step 3: Precipitating DNA from alcohol solution

The DNA is obtained by adding a cold ethanol solution that causes the DNA fragments to come together and precipitate. Because the DNA threads are sticky, they bind to a glass rod so they can be removed from the solution. Following the extraction of DNA, students will make observations and discuss the similarities and differences in DNA samples obtained from different sources.

Lab Information

Time: 2–3 hr
Comments: Tear out the report sheets and place them beside the matching procedures.
Related topics: Deoxyribonucleic acid, nitrogenous bases, deoxyribose, nucleosides, nucleotides,
               replication

Experimental Procedures

WEAR YOUR PROTECTIVE GOGGLES!

A. Components of DNA

Materials: organic model kits

A.1 Use the C, H, N, and O atoms in a model kit to make a model of one of the purines in DNA
nucleotides. Have another lab team make a model of the other purine. Draw the structures of the
purines found in the nucleotides of DNA. Save these models.

A.2 Use the C, H, and O atoms in a model kit to make a model of deoxyribose. Draw the structure of
deoxyribose. Save this model.

A.3 Use the P, H, and O atoms in a model kit to make a model of phosphate. Attach the phosphate
group and the purine you constructed to the deoxyribose sugar. Draw the structure of this
nucleotide. Write its name. Save this model.

A.4 With your neighbor lab team, combine two nucleotides to form a dinucleotide. Draw the structure
of this dinucleotide. Write its name. Combined the two nucleotides to make a different nucleotide.
Draw the structure of this dinucleotide.

B. Extraction of DNA

*Different student teams may extract DNA from different DNA sources and compare results or the
procedure may be run initially with onions and then repeated using a DNA source selected by each
student team.*

Materials: DNA sources: white onions, variety of other DNA plant sources such as cauliflower,
broccoli, garlic, split peas, bananas, and/or animal sources such as chicken liver, calf thymus.
Lab items: knife, two 250-mL beakers, thermometer, hot water bath (400-mL beaker about $\frac{1}{2}$ full
of water, iron ring, wire screen, and Bunsen burner), blender, cheesecloth or filter paper, microscope
Lab chemicals: SDS-NaCl-EDTA buffer solution (Your instructor will prepare this buffer: 50 g
sodium dodecyl sulfate, 50 g NaCl, 5 g sodium citrate, 0.2 mL of 0.5 MEDTA and water to make
1 L), isopropanol (placed in an ice bath to keep cold), citrate buffer (0.15 M NaCl, 0.015 M sodium
citrate)

1. Obtain about 50 g of a white onion or other DNA source. Use a knife to dice the onion or other
DNA source into small pieces. Place the pieces in a 250-mL beaker and add 50 mL of the extraction (SDS-NaCl-EDTA) buffer.

2. Prepare a hot water bath. Place the beaker in the hot water bath, and heat to 60°C. Maintain a temperature of about 60°C by adjusting or removing the flame of the heat source. Allow the beaker to remain in water at 60°C for 15 minutes. (Any longer time in hot water will start to break down DNA.) Stir the mixture occasionally. Remove the beaker and place it in an ice bath for 10 minutes.

Pour the cooled mixture into a blender and blend the contents for 60 seconds using 15-second bursts. Pour the mixture through two pieces of cheesecloth placed over a clean 250-mL beaker. This filtering may take as long as one hour. You may need to use new sets of cheesecloth as it becomes clogged with cell debris.

3. Measure the volume of the filtered onion liquid collected in the beaker and obtain an equal volume of ice-cold isopropanol. If the alcohol is not ice cold, cool it first in an ice bath. Holding the beaker at an angle, slowly pour the alcohol down the side. Allow the solution to sit for 2 minutes. An alcohol layer should form on the top of the filtrate. Because DNA is not soluble in alcohol, the whitish, viscous strands of DNA should precipitate out of the alcohol layer and form a whitish interface. (Other components of the mixture will remain soluble in the alcohol layer.)

Place a glass rod into the solution and turn it slowly to wind the DNA threads into a ball on the end of the glass rod. When you remove the glass rod the DNA will look like a viscous blob. Transfer the DNA from the glass rod to a paper towel and let it dry.

4. Observe the DNA obtained by other student teams with different DNA sources, or repeat the procedure above with another DNA source.

B.1 Observe texture and physical properties of the DNA you have extracted.

B.2 Examine the DNA under a microscope. Record your observations.

Report Sheet

Date _____   Name _____

Section _____   Team _____

Instructor _____

Pre-Lab Study Questions

1. Why does DNA have a slight negative charge?

2. What would homogenization and heating do to cell membranes?

A.   Components of DNA

Structures of Models (Lab Team 1)	Structures of Models (Lab Team 2)
A.1	A.1
A.2	A.2
A.3	A.3

(Continued)

Report Sheet

Structures of Models (Lab Team 1)	Structures of Models (Lab Team 2)
A.4	A.4

B. Extraction of DNA

DNA Source B.1	Texture and Appearance	B.2 Appearance under a microscope

Report Sheet

Questions and Problems

Q.1 Why is it necessary to heat the DNA source and buffer mixture?

Q.2 Why was an alcohol added to the filtered onion liquid?

Q.3 What similarities did you observe in the appearance of DNA from different DNA sources? Why?

Q.4 How would be DNA extracted from an onion be different from the DNA extracted from cauliflower? Why?

Q.5 Write the complementary base sequence for the following segment of DNA.

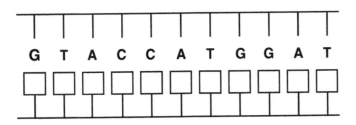

Appendix
Materials and Solutions

Standard Laboratory Materials

The following equipment is expected to be in the laboratory lockers or available from the laboratory stock and will not be listed in each experiment.

Aspirators	Hot plates
Beakers (50–400 mL)	Ice
Balances (top loading or centigram)	Iron rings
Büchner filtration apparatus and filter paper	Litmus paper
Bunsen burners	Metersticks
Burets (50 mL)	pH paper
Buret clamps	Ring stand
Clay triangles	Rulers
Containers for waste disposal	Shell vials
Crucible and cover	Stirring rods, glass
Distilled water (special faucet or containers)	Spatulas
Droppers	Stoppers
Evaporating dish	Test tubes (6", 8")
Flask, Erlenmeyer (125–250 mL)	Test tube rack
Filter paper for funnels	Thermometer
Funnel	Tongs (crucible and beaker)
Glass stirring rods	Watch glass
Gloves	Wire gauze
Graduated cylinders (5–250 mL)	

Materials Needed for Individual Experiments

The equipment and chemicals listed throughout the appendix are the materials needed in the laboratory to perform the experiments in this lab manual. The amounts given are recommended for 20–24 students working in teams.

Measurement and Significant Figures
A. Measuring Length
10   Lengths of string
B. Measuring Volume
3   Graduated cylinders partially filled with water and a few drops of food coloring
10   Metal solids
C. Measuring Mass
10   Unknown mass samples

Conversion Factors
A. Rounding Off
10   Solid objects with regular shapes
D. Conversion Factors for Volume
3   1-liter graduated cylinders
3   1-quart (or two 1-pint) measures
E. Conversion Factors for Mass
5   Commercial products with mass given on label in metric and U.S. system units

From *Essential Laboratory Manual for Chemistry: An Introduction to General, Organic, and Biological Chemistry*, Ninth Edition, Karen C. Timberlake. Copyright © 2007 by Pearson Education, Inc. Published by Benjamin Cummings. All rights reserved.

F. Measuring Temperature
200 g   Rock salt

Density and Specific Gravity
A. Density of a Solid
10   Metal objects (cubes or cylinders of aluminum, iron, lead, tin, zinc, etc.)
10   Large graduated cylinders to fit metal objects
10   Strings or threads (short lengths to tie around metal solids)
B. Density of a Liquid
200 mL Isopropyl alcohol   200 mL Corn syrup
200 mL 20% NaCl or 20% $CaCl_2$
200 mL Mineral water, vegetable oil, milk, juices, soft drinks, window cleaners, etc.
C. Specific Gravity
3–4   Hydrometers in graduated cylinders containing water and the liquids used for (B).

Atomic Structure and Electron Arrangement
A. Physical Properties of Elements
Display of elements (metals and nonmetals)
B. Periodic Table
Periodic tables, colored pencils
Display of elements
C. Flame Tests
10   Spot plates   10   Flame-test wires
10   Corks   200 mL 1 M HCl
100 mL Unknown solutions (2–3) in dropper bottles (same as test solutions)
Place in dropper bottles:
100 mL 0.1 M $CaCl_2$ 100 mL 0.1 M KCl
100 mL 0.1 M $BaCl_2$ 100 mL 0.1 M $SrCl_2$
100 mL 0.1 M $CuCl_2$ 100 mL 0.1 M NaCl

Nuclear Radiation
A. Background Count
1   Geiger-Müeller radiation detection tube
B. Radiation from Radioactive Sources
1   Geiger-Müeller radiation detection tube

3–4   Radioactive sources of alpha- and beta-radiation

Consumer products: Fiestaware®, minerals, old lantern mantles containing thorium compounds, camera lenses, old watches with radium-painted numbers on dials, fertilizers with P_2O, smoke detectors containing Am-241, anti-static devices for records and film containing Po-210, some foods such as salt substitute (KCl), cream of tartar, instant tea, instant coffee, dried seaweed
C. Effect of Shielding, Time and Distance
1   Geiger-Müeller radiation detection tube

5–6   Shielding materials such as lead sheets, paper, glass squares, cloth, cardboard

3–4   Radioactive sources used in 5B.

Compounds and their Formulas
Merck Index or *CRC Handbook of Chemistry and Physics*
B. Ionic Compounds and Formulas
$NaCl(s)$
C. Ionic Compounds with Transition Metals
$FeCl_3(s)$
D. Ionic Compounds with Polyatomic Ions
$K_2CO_3(s)$
E. Covalent (Molecular) Compounds
H_2O

Chemical Reactions and Equations
A. Magnesium and oxygen
10   Magnesium ribbon (2–3 cm)
B. Zinc and Copper(II) Sulfate
20   Pieces of zinc(s) strips, 1 cm square   100 mL 1 M $CuSO_4$
C. Metals and HCl
10   Cu pieces and Zn pieces 1 cm square   10 Mg ribbon pieces ~ 2 cm long
250 mL 1 M HCl
D. Reactions of Ionic Compounds
Place 100 mL each in dropper bottles:
0.1 M $CaCl_2$ 0.1 M Na_3PO_4
0.1 M $BaCl_2$ 0.1 M Na_2SO_4
0.1 M $FeCl_3$ 0.1 M KSCN
E. Sodium Carbonate and HCl
20   Wood splints   25 g $Na_2CO_3(s)$
250 mL 1 M HCl

Moles and Chemical Formulas
A. Finding the Simplest Formula
10   Heat-resistant pads
10   Mg ribbon (0.2–0.3 g, 16–18 cm strips)
          Steel wool
B. Formula of a Hydrate
10   Heat-resistant pads
100 g   Hydrate of $MgSO_4 \cdot 7H_2O$

Energy and Matter
A. A Heating Curve for Water
5   Timers
B. Energy in Changes of State
10   Styrofoam cups, covers
C. Food Calories
3–4   Food products with nutrition data on labels
D. Exothermic and Endothermic Reactions
50 g $NH_4NO_3(s)$
50 g $CaCl_2(s)$ anhydrous

Materials and Solutions

Gas Laws: Boyle's and Charles'
B. Charles' Law
10	One-hole stoppers to fit 125-mL Erlenmeyer flasks
10	Short pieces of glass
10	Short pieces of rubber tubing
10	Pinch clamps
10	Water pans
20	Boiling chips

Partial Pressures of Oxygen, Nitrogen, and Carbon Dioxide
A. Partial Pressures of Oxygen and Nitrogen in Air
25 g	Fe (iron) filings	Barometer

B. Carbon Dioxide in the Atmosphere
The following items may be assembled by instructor.
10	Glass tubing (60–75 cm)		
10	Two-hole stoppers with two short piece of glass tubing		
20	Rubber tubing (1 long, 1 short)	10	Pinch clamps
10 mL	Food coloring (optional)		
20 mL	Mineral oil	100 mL 6 M NaOH	

C. Carbon Dioxide in Expired Air
Use same items as in 11B.
20	Clean straws to fit rubber tubing

Solutions
A. Polarity of Solutes and Solvents (*May be a demonstration*)
20 g	KMnO$_4$(s)		20 g	I$_2$(s)
20 g	Sucrose(s)		200 mL	Cyclohexane
20 mL	Vegetable oil (2 dropper bottles)			

B. Solubility of KNO$_3$ (*Work in Teams*)
100 g	KNO$_3$(s)
10	Weighing papers

C. Concentration of a Sodium Chloride Solution
200 mL	NaCl solution (saturated)
5	10-mL pipets (*optional*)

Testing for Cations and Anions
A. Tests for Positive Ions (Cations)
10	Spot plates	10	Flame test wires
200 mL	3 M HCl	200 mL	6 M HNO$_3$
100 mL	6 M NaOH		

Place 100 mL each in dropper bottles:
0.1 M NaCl	0.1 M KCl
0.1 M CaCl$_2$	0.1 M (NH$_4$)$_2$C$_2$O$_4$
0.1 M NH$_4$Cl	0.1 M FeCl$_3$
0.1 M KSCN	

B. Test for Negative Ions (Anions)
Place 100 mL each in dropper bottles:
0.1 M NaCl	0.1 M AgNO$_3$
6 M HNO$_3$	3 M HCl
0.1 M Na$_2$SO$_4$	0.1 M BaCl$_2$
0.1 M Na$_3$PO$_4$	0.1 M Na$_2$CO$_3$

(NH₄)₂MoO₄ reagent

50 mL   Unknowns: KCl, Na₂CO₃, (NH₄)₂SO₄, CaCl₂, K₂SO₄, (NH₄)₃PO₄, etc.

Solutions, Colloids, and Suspensions

A. Identification Tests

200 mL 1% starch   200 mL 10% glucose

200 mL 10% NaCl   500 mL Benedict's reagent

Place the following in dropper bottles:

100 mL 0.1 *M* AgNO₃   100 mL Iodine solution

B. Dialysis

10   20-cm dialysis bag (cellophane tubing)

100 mL 10% NaCl   100 mL 10% glucose

100 mL 1% starch   100 mL 0.1 *M* AgNO₃

100 mL Benedict's solution   100 mL Iodine solution

C. Filtration

25 g   Powdered charcoal   200 mL 1% starch

100 mL Iodine solution   100 mL 0.1 *M* AgNO₃

100 mL Benedict's solution

Acids and Bases

A. pH Color Using Red Cabbage Indicator

1   Red cabbage

200 mL Buffers pH 1–13

B. Measurement of pH

2–3   pH meters   2–3   Wash bottles

2–3   Boxes Kimwipes   200 mL Cabbage indicator from part A

20 mL   Buffers (pH 4, pH 10)

Samples to test for pH: bring from home or have in lab. *Examples:* shampoo, hair conditioner, mouthwash, antacids, detergents, fruit juice, vinegar, cleaners, aspirin

C. Acetic Acid in Vinegar

10   5-mL pipet and bulbs   200 mL Vinegar (white)

1L   0.1 *M* NaOH (standardized) 100 mL Phenolphthalein indicator

Properties of Organic Compounds

A. Color, Odor, and Physical State *(May be a display in lab)*

1–2   Chemistry handbook   20 g   NaCl(*s*)

20 g   KI(*s*)   20 g   Benzoic acid(*s*)

20 mL   Toluene   20 mL   cyclohexane

B. Solubility *(This may be an instructor demonstration.)*

20 g   NaCl(*s*)

20 mL   Toluene

20 mL   Cyclohexane

C. Combustion *(This may be an instructor demonstration.)*

30   Wood splints

10 g   NaCl(*s*)

10 mL   Cyclohexane

D. Structures of Alkanes, E. Isomers, and F. Cycloalkanes

10   Organic model kits or prepared models

2   Chemistry handbooks

Materials and Solutions

Alcohols, Aldehydes, and Ketones

A. Structures of Alcohols and Phenol
10   Organic model kits or prepared models

Use for B. and C.

50 mL	Ethanol	50 mL	*t*-butyl alcohol (2-methyl-2-propanol)
50 mL	Cyclohexanol	50 mL	2-propanol
50 mL	20% phenol		

C. Oxidation of Alcohols
100 mL   2% chromate solution

D, E, and F. Properties of Aldehydes and Ketones

50 mL	Acetone	50 mL	Benzaldehyde
50 g	Camphor	50 mL	Cinnamaldehyde,
50 mL	Vanillin	50 mL	Propionaldehyde (propanal)
50 mL	Cyclohexanone	50 mL	2,3-Butanedione
2	Chemistry handbooks		

E. Iodoform Test for Methyl Ketones (Test tubes from part D.3)
Use compounds from D

100 mL	10% NaOH	200 mL	Iodine test reagent

F. Oxidation of Aldehydes and Ketones
Use compounds from D

                                         500 mL   Benedict's reagent

Carboxylic Acids and Esters

A. Carboxylic Acids and Their Salts

100 mL	10% NaOH	100 mL	10% HCl
50 mL	Glacial acetic acid	50 g	Benzoic acid

B. Esters
10   Organic model sets

200 mL	Glacial acetic acid		
20 mL	Methanol	50 g	Salicylic acid
20 mL	1-Octanol	20 mL	1-Pentanol
20 mL	1-Propanol	50 mL	85% H_3PO_4 (dropper bottle)
		20 mL	Benzyl alcohol

C. Preparation of Aspirin

10	Pans or large beakers	50 g	Salicylic acid(s)
100 mL	Acetic anhydride	50 mL	85% H_3PO_4 in a dropper bottle

Carbohydrates

A. B Monosaccharides; Disaccharides
10   Organic model kits or prepared models

D. Benedict's Test for Reducing Sugars
500 mL   Benedict's reagent

50 mL each in dropper bottles:

2% glucose   2% fructose   2% sucrose   2% lactose   2% starch

E. Seliwanoff's Test for Ketohexoses
100 mL   Seliwanoff's reagent

50 mL each in dropper bottles:

2% glucose   2% fructose   2% sucrose   2% lactose   2% starch

F. Fermentation Test

6 Fermentation tubes (or 6 small test tubes and 6 large test tubes),

40 g Baker's yeast (fresh)

50 mL each in dropper bottles:

2% glucose   2% fructose   2% sucrose   2% lactose   2% starch

G. Iodine Test for Polysaccharides

10 Spot plates

100 mL Iodine reagent

50 mL each in dropper bottles:

2% glucose   2% fructose   2% sucrose   2% lactose   2% starch

H. Hydrolysis of Disaccharides and Polysaccharides

10 Spot plate (or watch glasses)

100 mL 10% NaOH   100 mL 10% HCl

100 mL Iodine reagent   500 mL Benedict's reagent

50 mL each in dropper bottles: 2% sucrose   2% starch

Lipids

A. Triacylglycerols

5 Organic model kits or prepared models

B. Physical Properties of Some Lipids and Fatty Acids

25 g Lecithin   25 g Stearic acid

25 g Cholesterol   100 mL Methylene chloride, CH_2Cl_2

Place 25 mL each in dropper bottles:

   Oleic acid   Vitamin A

   Olive oil   Safflower oil

C. Bromine Test for Unsaturation

5 Organic model kits or models Samples from B

100 mL 1% Br_2 in CH_2Cl_2

D. Preparation of Hand Lotion

Team project: Steps D.1, D.2, and D.3 may be prepared by different teams in the lab.

10 10-mL graduated cylinders   20 50-mL or 100-mL beakers

50g stearic acid   15 g cetyl alcohol

25 g lanolin (anhydrous)   15 mL (dropper) triethanolamine

25 mL glycerin   100 mL ethanol

100 mL distilled water   fragrance (optional)

commercial hand lotion products

Saponification and Soaps

A. Saponification

Place in dropper bottles:

100 mL Methyl salicylate   100 mL 10% NaOH

100 mL 10% HCl

B. Saponification: Preparation of Soap

Optional: Hot plate and a stirring bar   200 mL Ethanol

100 mL 20% NaOH   200 mL Saturated NaCl solution

10 pairs of disposable gloves

100 g Solid fats: lard, coconut oil, solid shortening, coconut oil

100 mL Liquid vegetable oil, olive or other vegetable oil

C. Properties of Soap and Detergents

50g Commercial soaps, lab-prepared soap (from part B), 50 g Detergent

50 mL Safflower oil   100 mL 1% $CaCl_2$

100 mL 1% $MgCl_2$ 100 mL 1% $FeCl_3$

Materials and Solutions

Amines and Amino Acids

A. Solubility of Amines in Water
Place in dropper bottles:

30 mL   Aniline
30 mL   *N*-Methylaniline

30 mL   Triethylamine

B. Neutralization of Amines with Acids
Test tubes from part A

100 mL 10% HCl

C. Amino Acids
10   Organic model kits or prepared models

D. Chromatography of Amino Acids

1 box   Plastic wrap

50   Toothpicks or capillary tubing

2   Hair dryers (optional)

1 box   Whatman #1 chromatograph
          paper (12 cm × 24 cm)

1   Drying oven (80 ℃)

1   Stapler

Place 50 mL each in dropper bottles:

1% Alanine

1% Serine

1% Lysine

1% Glutamic acid

1% Aspartic acid

1% Phenylalanine

50 mL   1% Unknown amino acids (Use samples from above list)

Chromatography solvent

100 mL 0.5 *M* NH_4OH

200 mL isopropyl alcohol

0.2% Ninhydrin spray reagent (in ethanol or acetone)

Peptide and Proteins

A. Peptide Bonds and B. Structure of Proteins
5   Organic model set

C. Denaturation of Proteins
Place in dropper bottle:

100 mL 1% egg albumin

Dissolve 1 g egg albumin in water to make 100 mL or students can make a fresh egg albumin solution by mixing the egg white from one egg with 200 mL of water and filtering the mixture through cheesecloth into a beaker.

100 mL 10% HNO_3
100 mL 95% ethanol

100 mL 10% NaOH
100 mL 1% $AgNO_3$

D. Isolation of Casein (Milk Protein)
200 mL Nonfat milk

200 mL 10% acetic acid

E. Color Tests for Proteins
10 g   Casein from part D

Place 100 ml each in dropper bottles:

1% Glycine

1% Gelatin

10% NaOH

1 can   0.2% Ninhydrin reagent

1% Tyrosine

1% Egg albumin (See part C.)

50 mL   Conc. HNO_3

200 mL 5% $CuSO_4$

Enzymes

A. Effect of Enzyme Concentration

10   Spot plate (or plastic sheets)

10   Timer

200 mL Amylase preparation

100 mL Iodine reagent

1% starch (buffered to pH 7)

100 mL 1% Glucose

500 mL Benedict's reagent

B. Effect of Temperature
 Amylase preparation
 100 mL Iodine test reagent

200 mL 1% Starch

C. Effect of pH
 Amylase preparation
 200 mL 1% Starch

100 mL buffers (pH 2, 4, 7, 10)
100 mL Iodine test reagent

D. Inhibition of Enzyme Activity
 Amylase preparation
 Place 50 mL each in dropper bottles:
   1% NaCl
   1% $CuSO_4$
   1% $HgCl_2$
 200 mL 1% Starch

1% $AgNO_3$
1% $Pb(NO3)_2$
Ethanol
100 mL Iodine reagent

DNA Components and Extraction

A. Components of DNA

10 organic model kits

B. Extraction of DNA

Different student teams may extract DNA from different DNA sources and compare results or the procedure may be run initially with onions and then repeated using other DNA sources selected by each student team.

DNA sources: white onions, cauliflower, broccoli, garlic, split peas, bananas, and/or animal sources such as chicken liver, calf thymus

5	knives	2	blenders
	cheesecloth or filter paper, ice	1-2	microscopes
1 L	SDS-NaCl-EDTA buffer solution (50 g sodium dodecyl sulfate, 50 g NaCl, 5 g sodium citrate, 0.2 mL of 0.5 EDTA and water to make 1 L)		

500 mL isopropanol (in an ice bath)

Preparation of Solutions Used in the Laboratory

Acids and bases

Ammonium hydroxide NH_4OH
 0.5 *M* NH_4OH Dilute 34 mL conc. NH_4OH with water to make 1.0 L

Acetic acid $C_2H_3O_2$(HAc)
 10% HAc Dilute 50 mL of glacial HAc with water to make 500 mL

Hydrochloric acid HCl
 1.0 HCl Dilute 85 mL conc. HCl with water to make 1.0 L
 3.0 *M* HCl Dilute 250 mL conc. HCl with water to make 1.0 L
 10% HCl Dilute 230 mL conc. HCl to make 1.0 L

Nitric acid HNO_3
 6 *M* HNO_3 Dilute 76 mL conc. HNO_3 with water to make 200 mL
 10% HNO_3 Dilute 10 mL conc. HNO_3 with water to make 100 mL

Materials and Solutions

Sodium hydroxide NaOH

0.1 M NaOH Dissolve 4.0 g NaOH in water to make 1.0 L
Standardization: Weigh a 1-g sample of potassium hydrogen phthalate, $KC_8H_5O_4$, to 0.001 g. Dissolve in 25 mL of water, add phenolphthalein indicator, and titrate with the prepared NaOH solution. Calculate the molarity (3 significant figures) as

$$\text{g phthalate} \times \frac{1 \text{ mole phthalate}}{204 \text{ g phthalate}} \times \frac{1}{\text{L NaOH used}} = \underline{\qquad} M$$

6 M NaOH   Dissolve 240 g NaOH in water to make 1.0 L
10% NaOH   Dissolve 10 g NaOH in water to make 100 mL
20% NaOH   Dissolve 20 g NaOH in water to make 100 mL

Salt solutions

Ammonium chloride   0.1 M NH_4Cl Dissolve 0.54 g NH_4Cl in water to make 100 mL

Ammonium molybdate   Dissolve 8.1 g H_2MoO_4 in 20 mL water. Add 6 mL conc. NH_4OH to give a saturated solution. Filter. Slowly add filtrate to a mixture of 27 mL conc. HNO_3 and 40 mL water. Let stand 1 day. Filter and add water to 100 mL.

Ammonium oxalate   0.1 M $(NH_4)_2C_2O_4$ Dissolve 1.4 g $(NH_4)_2C_2O_4 \bullet H_2O$ with water to make 100 mL

Barium chloride   0.1 M $BaCl_2$ Dissolve 2.4 g $BaCl_2 \bullet 2H_2O$ in water to make 100 mL

Calcium chloride
1% $CaCl_2$ Dissolve 1.3 g $CaCl_2 \bullet 2H_2O$ in water to make 100 mL
20% $CaCl_2$ Dissolve 200 g $CaCl_2$ in water to make 1.0 L
0.1 M $CaCl_2$ Dissolve 1.5 g $CaCl_2 \bullet 2H_2O$ in water to make 100 mL

Copper(II) chloride   0.1 M $CuCl_2$ Dissolve 1.7 g $CuCl_2 \bullet 2H_2O$ in water to make 100 mL

Copper(II) sulfate
1 M $CuSO_4$ Dissolve 25 g $CuSO_4 \bullet 5H_2O$ in water to make 100 mL
5% $CuSO_4$ Dissolve 15.6 g $CuSO_4 \bullet 5H_2O$ in water to give 200 mL

Iron(III) chloride
0.1 M $FeCl_3$ Dissolve 2.7 g $FeCl_3 \bullet 6 H_2O$ in water to make 100 mL
1% $FeCl_3$ Dissolve 1.7 g $FeCl_3 \bullet 6H_2O$ in water to give 100 mL

Lead(II) nitrate   1% $Pb(NO_3)_2$ Dissolve 0.5 g $Pb(NO_3)_2$ in water to make 50 mL

Magnesium chloride   1% $MgCl_2$ Dissolve 2.1 g $MgCl_2 \bullet 6H_2O$ in water to make 100 mL

Mercury(II) chloride   1% $HgCl_2$ Dissolve 0.5 g $HgCl_2$ in water to make 100 mL

Potassium chloride   0.1 M KCl   Dissolve 0.75 g KCl in water to make 100 mL

Potassium thiocyanate   0.1 M KSCN   Dissolve 1 g KSCN in water to make 100 mL

Silver nitrate
0.1 M $AgNO_3$ Dissolve 1.7 g $AgNO_3$ in water to make 100 mL
1% $AgNO_3$ Dissolve 0.5 g $AgNO_3$ in water to make 50 mL

Sodium carbonate   0.1 M Na_2CO_3 Dissolve 2.9 g $Na_2CO_3 \bullet 7H_2O$ in water to make 100 mL

Sodium chloride	0.1 M NaCl	Dissolve 0.58 g NaCl in water to make 100 mL
	1% NaCl	Dissolve 1 g NaCl in water to make 100 mL
	10% NaCl	Dissolve 10 g NaCl in water to make 100 mL
	20% NaCl	Dissolve 200 g NaCl in water to make 1.0 L
	Saturated NaCl	Add 80 g NaCl to water to make 200 mL

| Sodium phosphate | 0.1 M Na_3PO_4 | Dissolve 3.8 g $Na_3PO_4 \cdot 12H_2O$ in water to make 100 mL |

| Sodium sulfate | 0.1 M Na_2SO_4 | Dissolve 3.2 g $Na_2SO_4 \cdot 10H_2O$ in water to make 100 mL |

| Strontium chloride | 0.1 M $SrCl_2$ | Dissolve 1.95 g $SrCl_2 \cdot 2H_2O$ in water to make 100 mL |

Carbohydrates

| Fructose | 2% fructose | Add 1 g fructose to water to make 50 mL |

Glucose	0.1 M glucose	Dissolve 1.8 g glucose in water to make 100 mL
	2% glucose	Add 1 g glucose to water to make 50 mL
	10% glucose	Dissolve 10 g glucose in water to make 100 mL

| Lactose | 2% lactose | Add 1 g lactose to water to make 50 mL |

| Sucrose | 0.1 M sucrose | Dissolve 3.42 g sucrose in water to make 100 mL |
| | 2% sucrose | Add 1 g sucrose to water to make 50 mL |

| Starch | 1% | Make a paste of 2 g soluble starch and 40 mL water. Add to 160 mL of boiling water to make 200 mL. Stir and cool. |
| | 2% | Make a paste of 4 g soluble starch and 40 mL water. Add to 160 mL of boiling water to make 200 mL. Stir and cool. |

Reagents

Benedict's reagent — Dissolve 86 g sodium citrate, $Na_3C_6H_5O_7$, and 50 g anhydrous Na_2CO_3 in 400 mL water. Warm. Dissolve 8.6 g $CuSO_4 \cdot 5H_2O$ in 50 mL water. Add to sodium citrate solution, stir, and add water to make 500 mL solution.

Seliwanoff's reagent — Dissolve 0.15 g resorcinol in 100 mL 6 M HCl

Iodine solution (starch test) — Dissolve 10 g I_2 + 20 g KI in water to make 500 mL

Iodine solution (iodoform) — Dissolve 10 g I_2 + 20 g KI in water to make 100 mL

0.2% Ninhydrin — Dissolve 0.2 g in ethanol to make 100 mL

20% Phenol — Dissolve 20 g phenol in water to make 100 mL

Indicators

1% Bromine solution — Dilute 1 ml Br_2 with methylene chloride to make 100 mL

2% Chromate — Dissolve 2.0 g $K_2Cr_2O_7$ in 10 mL of 6 M H_2SO_4; then carefully add to water to make 100 mL

1% Phenolphthalein — Dissolve 1 g phenolphthalein in 50 mL ethanol and 50 mL water

Materials and Solutions

Amino acids

1% Alanine	Dissolve 0.5 g alanine in water to make 50 mL
1% Aspartic acid	Dissolve 0.5 g aspartic acid in water to make 50 mL
1% Glutamic acid	Dissolve 0.5 g glutamic acid in water to make 50 mL
1% Lysine	Dissolve 0.5 g lysine in water to make 50 mL
1% Phenylalanine	Dissolve 0.5 g phenylalanine in water to make 50 mL
1% Serine	Dissolve 0.5 g serine in water to make 50 mL